An Early Start to the Environment

Roy Richards

SIMON & SCHUSTER

LONDON • SYDNEY • NEW YORK • TOKYO • SINGAPORE • TORONTO

Text © Roy Richards 1991
Artwork © The artists 1991

First published in Great Britain in 1991 by
Simon & Schuster Ltd
Wolsey House, Wolsey Road
Hemel Hempstead HP2 4SS

Printed in Great Britain by
BPCC Hazell Books, Paulton and Aylesbury

British Library Cataloguing in Publication Data
Richards, Roy
  An early start to the environment.
  1. Environment
  333.7

ISBN 0-7501-0120-2

Series editor: John Day
Editor: Jane Glendening
Design and all artwork except that listed below:
Anna Hancock
James Field/Simon Girling & Associates: pages 22,
23 (far left), 24, 25, 26, 38 (centre), 40 (except
bottom right), 44, 45, 52, 53, 54, 57, 63, 67, 68
(bottom right), 69, 84, 90, 92
Jeff Edwards: pages 42, 51 (except top left), 58
(except bottom left), 68 (except bottom right), 81,
82 (left)

Looking at places can tell us both how they work and something of their past. In environmental studies children explore the area around them. Investigating the nature of the materials used in buildings, finding out about the plants and animals around the school and collecting information about the weather engages children in scientific studies. Looking at the relationship of people to an area and the things that they do there, together with the general mapping of buildings and the relationship of settlement to features in the landscape, involves geographical skills. Any local study must also touch on things from the past: be it the development of the local parish church, an old milestone found by the side of the road or a look at Victorian schooling arising from a study of the Victorian buildings in which many schools are still housed.

This book interweaves such scientific, geographical and historical aspects of the curriculum in such a way as to relate strongly to children, to their immediate environment and to the cross-curricula approach to learning common in primary schools.

The roots of a feeling for conservation and a proper care for the Earth come from studying the environment although, of course, they are not the only reason for such study. Children learn through contact with their world – they get to know it and begin to understand relationships within it.

This experience is at first hand and is highly personal, for impressions come crowding in. Children are constantly trying to make sense of these – selecting and ordering them, often subconsciously.

Part of the art of teaching is to create the opportunities for such experiences. This book describes a host of situations in the local environment which can help bring about sound learning and offer experiences that will stay with the children for the rest of their lives.

As in other books in this series children are introduced to the processes of:
- exploring their environment in order to gather experiences at first hand
- manipulating objects and materials
- observing things around them
- questioning and arguing about things
- testing things out and performing simple problem solving activities
- looking for patterns and relationships.

National Curriculum
Science Curriculum
Attainment Target 1 (Exploration of Science) permeates many of the activities in this book, which encourages the processes of science. Within the activities described there is much to observe, describe, test out, gather information on, analyse and draw conclusions on.

The following Attainment Targets are considered in various ways:
AT 2   The variety of life
AT 3   Process of life
AT 4   Genetics and evolution
AT 5   Human influences on Earth
AT 6   Types and uses of materials
AT 9   Earth and atmosphere
AT 10 Forces
AT 11 Electricity and magnetism
AT 14 Sound and music
AT 15 Using light and electromagnetic radiation

This list is based on the Science Attainment Targets as they stood at the time of printing.

History Curriculum
There are many activities throughout the book which will help to develop a child's sense of the past: the theme which predominates the programme of study for Key Stage 1.

For Key Stage 2, there are many activities which fit in with two of the Core Study Units:
CSU 3 Victorian Britain
CSU 4 Britain since 1930

Geography Curriculum
There is a contribution to each of the five Attainment Targets. These are:
AT 1   Geographical skills
AT 2   Knowledge and understanding of places
AT 3   Physical geography
AT 4   Human geography
AT 5   Environmental geography

Conservation
It is now illegal to pick many wild flowers and proper conservation of both plant and animal life is essential. The Department of the Environment publishes a leaflet on 'Protecting Britain's Wildlife', which lists protected animals and plants. This is available from the Department of the Environment/Transport, Distribution Centre, Victoria Road, Ruislip HA4 0NZ. Magazines about the countryside are a good way of keeping up to date with recent legislation.

Safety in schools
All the activities in this book are safe provided they are properly organised and supervised in accordance with the recommendations of the DES, the Health and Safety Executive, the Association for Science Education, and local authority regulations. Any teachers who are uncertain about safety in scientific and technical work should consult their LEA advisers. They should also read 'Be safe: some aspects of safety in science and technology in primary schools', published by the Association for Science Education.

Always pack away potentially dangerous apparatus and chemicals immediately the activity is over

Red triangles
Some activities in this book do require extra care and attention. They are marked with a red triangle. Under no circumstances should children be allowed to pursue them unsupervised, particularly during breaks.

Roy Richards

Is the school new or old?

Make some sketches.

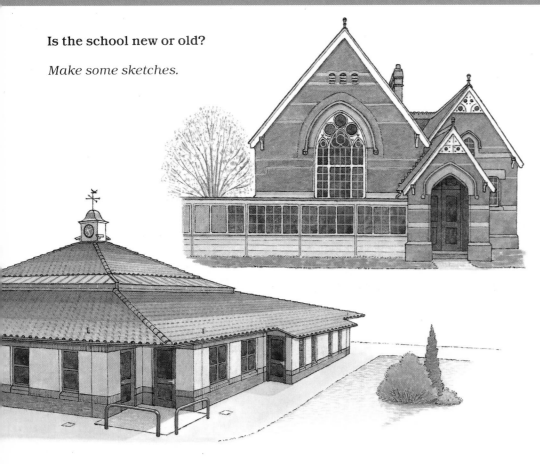

Survey the materials used

Look for brick, stone, concrete, tiles, slates, wood, metal, glass, plaster and roughcast concrete.

Make a table.

Material	Use	Structural or decorative	Where found

Markings on the playground

Make a record of all the markings found on the playground.

Look for wear and tear

Make sketches.

steps worn

corners of wall worn away

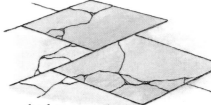

cracked paving stones

holes in tarmac

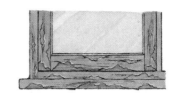

paint flaking from window frames

rusting railings

Look for colours

Colour	Where found
red	rooftiles, bricks
white	window frames
blue	

Which are the three most common colours?

Make a plan of the school and playground

Use a surveyor's tape or a 10 metre length of string marked at 1 metre intervals.

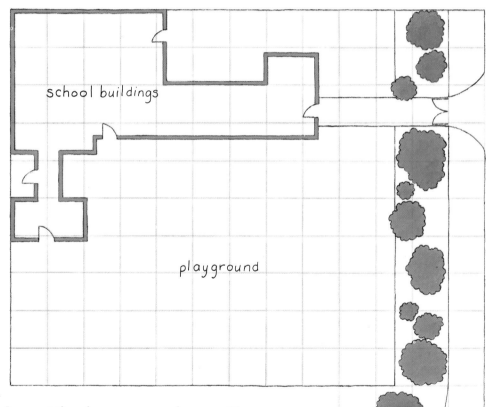

school buildings

playground

Lay out the plan on squared paper. Choose a suitable scale.

Use the plan to work out the area covered by the school buildings and by the playground. Work out the school perimeter. Work out the perimeters of the buildings and the playground.

Find out the height of the school

Make a clinometer from a protractor and a drinking straw, with a Plasticine plumb bob.

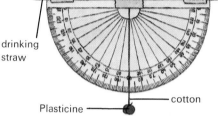

drinking straw

Plasticine — cotton

Measure angle A and distance x. Construct a scale drawing to give you height y. Don't forget to add on the height h of the observer to give you the true height of the building.

Litter black spots

Plot the litter black spots around the school.

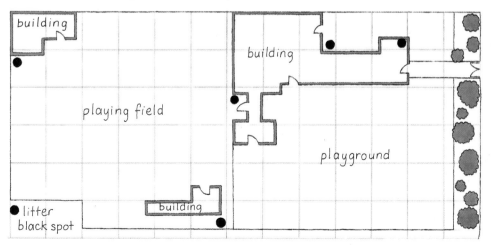

building

building

playing field

playground

litter black spot

building

Where would it be best to put litter bins?

Investigate animals around the school

Keep records. Use a clipboard.

Look at:

plants and fruits

tree stumps

fungi

water

tree leaves

grass

Look in and under:

rotting logs

stones

leaf litter

bricks

Record your results.

Date	Weather		
Animal	Found on	Animal	Found in or under

Sort your animals into groups

Animals with no legs

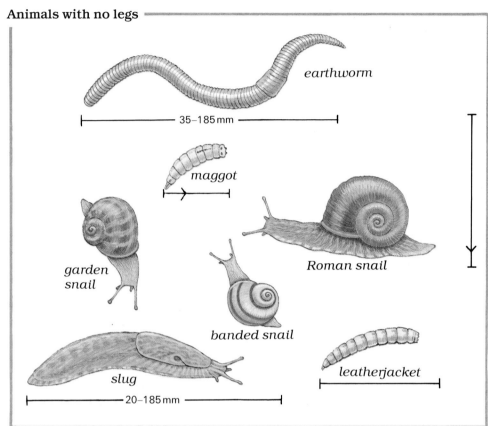

earthworm

35–185 mm

maggot

garden snail

banded snail

Roman snail

slug

20–185 mm

leatherjacket

Animals with six legs in front and some sucker feet behind

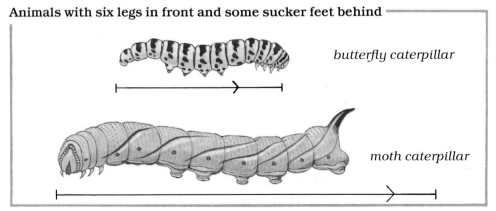

butterfly caterpillar

moth caterpillar

Animals with six legs

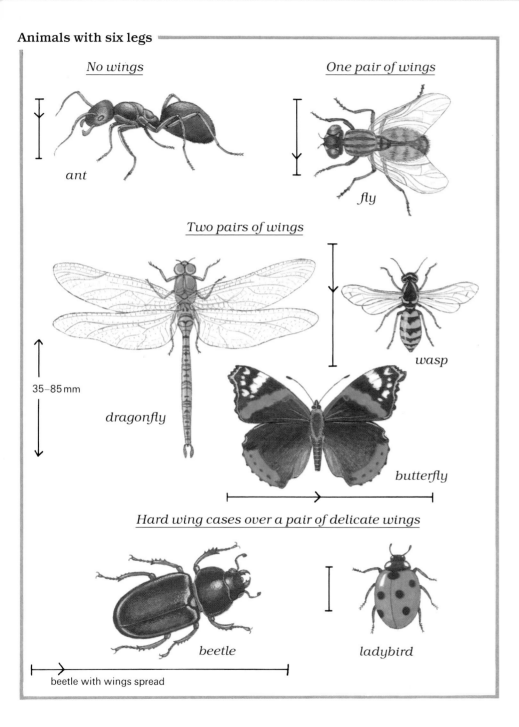

No wings

ant

One pair of wings

fly

Two pairs of wings

35–85 mm

dragonfly

wasp

butterfly

Hard wing cases over a pair of delicate wings

beetle

ladybird

beetle with wings spread

Animals with eight legs

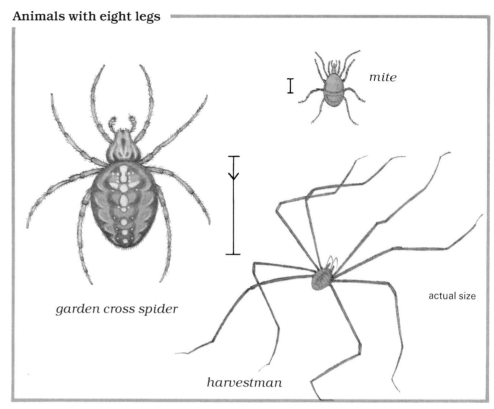

mite

garden cross spider

actual size

harvestman

Animals with lots of legs all alike

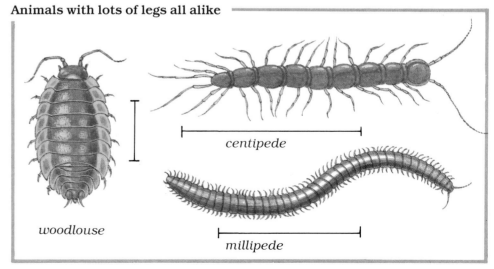

woodlouse

centipede

millipede

Collecting animals

Great care must be taken in handling animals.

Plastic spoons, small paint brushes and pooters are all useful. Small clear plastic boxes are handy for storing the catch. Always return the catch to the wild as soon as possible.

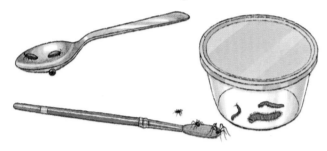

Some of the catch, for example caterpillars, can often be successfully reared if you know the plant that they feed on.

Collecting in long grass

Sweep the net through the grass, rather as you would sweep a lawn with a besom.

Collecting from leaf litter

Sieve soil and leaf litter from under trees and bushes.

Pitfall traps

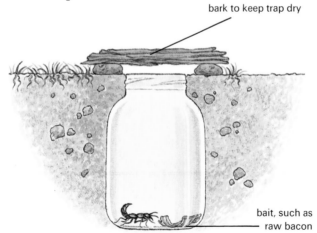

bark to keep trap dry

bait, such as raw bacon

A jam jar sunk into the ground makes a good trap. It will tend to catch active carnivorous invertebrates.

Experiment with different kinds of bait.

Collecting from trees

Shake a branch above a white sheet.

Mites, spiders, caterpillars, midges and so on will fall on to the sheet.

Use a pooter to pick up the smallest of these animals.

suck here

muslin to stop you sucking up insect

Collecting from ponds

See 'An Early Start to Nature' (pages 48–49, 52–55).

Don't worry too much about identifying the individual invertebrates that you collect, concentrate on sorting them into groups.

Compare two areas

For a fair comparison children will need to think about how long they visit each area, its size and the time of day when they visit.

Compare:
 under shrubs with a herbaceous border
 open grassland with tree foliage.

Keep a record.

Animal	Number found			
	First visit		Second visit	
	Area 1	Area 2	Area 1	Area 2
worms				
maggots				
leather jackets				
snails				
slugs				
bees / wasps				
butterflies / moths				
caterpillars				
flies				
beetles				

Make a book about the small animals that you find. Make sets to show the number of legs they have.

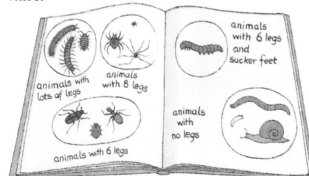

Plant galls

Oak-apple gall
A gall arises as the result of an attack by a bacterium, a fungus, a mite or an insect. One of the most common insect galls is the oak-apple gall caused by the gall wasp (*Biorhiza pallida*).

The gall wasp has a complex life cycle.

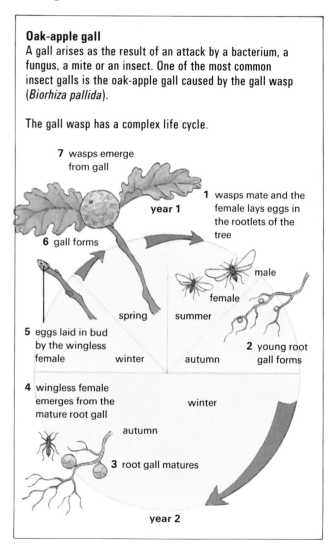

7 wasps emerge from gall
year 1
1 wasps mate and the female lays eggs in the rootlets of the tree
6 gall forms
male
female
spring summer
2 young root gall forms
5 eggs laid in bud by the wingless female
winter autumn
4 wingless female emerges from the mature root gall
winter
autumn
3 root gall matures
year 2

Look for galls around the school.

Other activities

See 'An Early Start to Nature' (pages 36–37, 40–47) for suggestions of things to find out about the animals that you collect.

Flower survey

Make a survey of the flowers around the school.

Make a bar chart showing the height of flowers around the area.

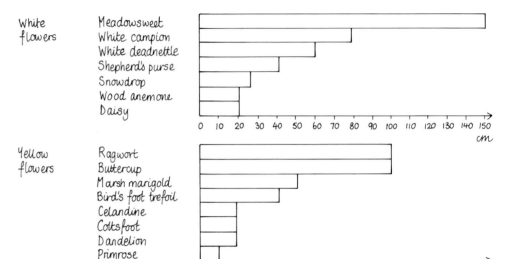

White flowers: Meadowsweet, White campion, White deadnettle, Shepherd's purse, Snowdrop, Wood anemone, Daisy

Yellow flowers: Ragwort, Buttercup, Marsh marigold, Bird's foot trefoil, Celandine, Coltsfoot, Dandelion, Primrose

Watch the animal visitors to flowers.

Plant:	Date:	Time: from	to
Weather: (circle the best words)	Raining / not raining Windy / some wind / no wind	Hot / warm / cold Sunny / some sun / not sunny	Humid / dry
Name of animal	How long it stayed	Part of plant visited	What it did

Key

Appearance

U – upright plant   Cl – climber

Ro – rosette   Ev – evergreen

Cr – creeper   L – low herb

Fruit dispersal

P – plumes   C – censer

W – wings   Ex – explosion

H – hooks   S – very small and light

Name of flower	Colour	Appearance	Where found					Month in			Dispersal of fruit
			Lawn	Dug ground	Waste ground	Cracks & paths	Other	Bud	Flower	Fruit	
Shepherd's purse	white	L		✓	✓						S
Groundsel	yellow	L		✓	✓						S
Daisy	white	Ro	✓		✓	✓		March			P
Dandelion	yellow	Ro	✓		✓	✓		March			P

Woodland flora

If there are trees in the school grounds or nearby, examine the different layers making up woodland flora.

There are four main layers: tree, shrub, herb, and a ground layer of mosses and lichens. Climbers make a fifth group.

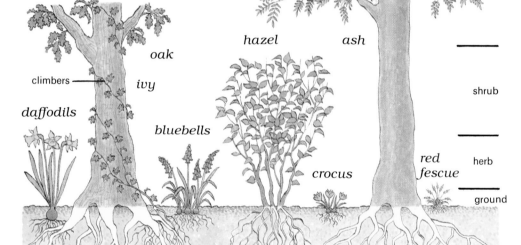

oak
ivy
climbers
daffodils
bluebells
hazel
ash
crocus
red fescue
tree
shrub
herb
ground

Make a classroom display that shows the different layers.

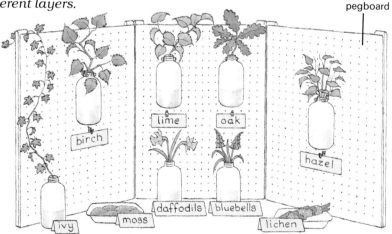

pegboard

birch
lime
oak
hazel
ivy
moss
daffodils
bluebells
lichen

In spring make drawings of the twigs. Stand the twigs in water and record their progress as the buds open.

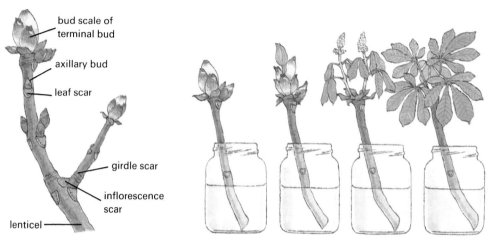

bud scale of terminal bud
axillary bud
leaf scar
girdle scar
inflorescence scar
lenticel

Record the flowering period of the herb layer through the year. Keep your record sheet pinned up in a corner of the classroom for easy access month by month.

Flower	Jan	Feb	Mar	Apr	May	Jun	Jul	Aug	Sep	Oct	Nov	Dec
Daffodil												
Bluebell												
Crocus												
Dandelion												
Daisy												
Buttercup												
Coltsfoot												
Red fescue												

More work

For more investigations on trees and other plants, and the animals associated with them, see 'An Early Start to Nature' (pages 8–27).

Make a 3D model of the classroom

Use a cardboard carton of roughly the same proportions as the classroom.

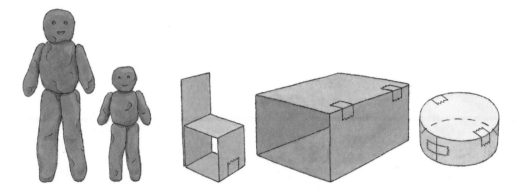

Use card to make the furniture. Make it in the shape of prisms.

Young children find it difficult to judge the scale. Make Plasticine models of the teacher and children. The children can then make the furniture to fit the models.

Make a plan of the classroom

Older children can do this.

Plans are relatively easy to make if you cut tables and chairs to scale from card. One centimetre to a metre is often suitable.

The furniture can then be quickly and approximately arranged in a classroom outline drawn to the same scale.

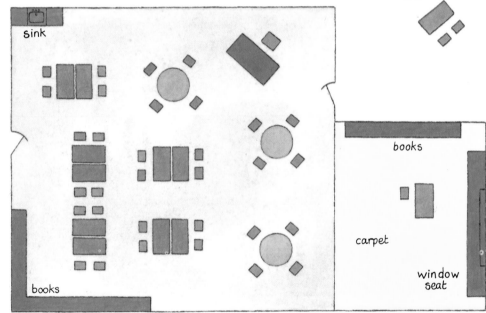

sink

books

carpet

window seat

books

The oldest children can mark off each wall in metre strips and take co-ordinates in order to position the furniture accurately.

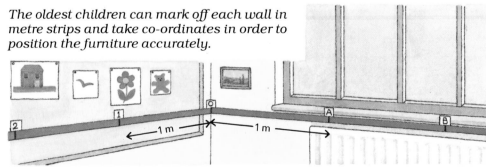

1 m   1 m

Record classroom temperature

Do this a number of times throughout the day.

Take the temperature in different parts of the classroom. If possible, leave a thermometer permanently in each place. Keep the height of the thermometer above the floor constant.

Place	Time	Temperature
Near door 1m above floor	9.00 11.00 1.00 3.00 home time	
Above radiator 1m above floor	9.00 11.00 1.00 3.00 home time	
Near window 1m above floor	9.00 11.00 1.00 3.00 home time	

Now take the temperature at different heights.

Plot your results as a series of graphs.

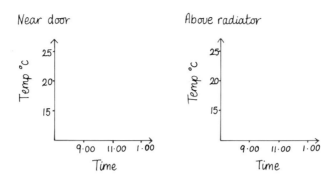

Discuss the results. Could the classroom be better insulated? How could you keep the classroom warmer or cooler?

Waste paper

Survey the paper thrown out at the end of each day.

What kinds of paper are thrown away? How much is thrown away?

Keep a record.

Date :		
Kind of paper	Amount thrown away	Paper not used
writing paper		
sugar paper		
card		

Also survey the staffroom, the headteacher's room and the secretary's office.

Recycling paper

Take some of the waste paper and tear it into small pieces. Mix the pieces with water.

Spread the pulp evenly over stretched muslin. Leave it to dry.

The result will be a form of paper.

See 'An Early Start to Technology' (page 74) for more information on paper making.

Force meters

Do drawers stick in your school? Are some doors easier to open than others?

Make some devices to measure pushes and pulls around the school. Such instruments are called force meters.

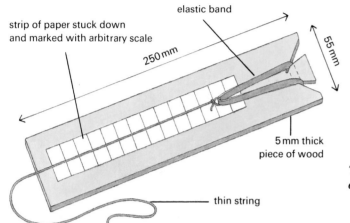

elastic band

strip of paper stuck down and marked with arbitrary scale

250 mm

55 mm

5 mm thick piece of wood

thin string

Tie the string to a door handle. The stretch in the elastic will give a measure of the pull.

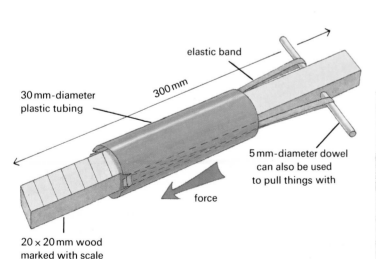

elastic band

30 mm-diameter plastic tubing

300 mm

5 mm-diameter dowel can also be used to pull things with

force

20 × 20 mm wood marked with scale

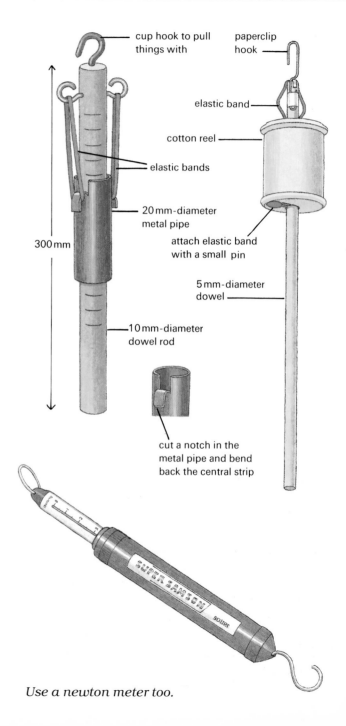

cup hook to pull things with

paperclip hook

elastic band

cotton reel

elastic bands

20 mm-diameter metal pipe

attach elastic band with a small pin

5 mm-diameter dowel

300 mm

10 mm-diameter dowel rod

cut a notch in the metal pipe and bend back the central strip

SUPER SAMSON

Use a newton meter too.

Make a survey

Push doors shut. Is it easier if you push near the door handle or near the hinge?

If the elastic stretches too easily use thicker bands.

Be careful. *If the elastic breaks, the force meter will spring back.*

Door	Push at handle	Push at hinge
Classroom		
Corridor		
Toilet		
Staffroom		

Pull drawers open.

Drawer	Pull
Tidy drawer	
Desk	
Secretary's	

Road safety

The force with which a moving vehicle hits a person can be enormous. Drawing children's attention to this through safe practical tests in the classroom will help with road safety.

Devise a force meter to register the force exerted by toy vehicles running down a slope.

Use a piece of card glued or pinned to a dowel rod. Mark an arbitrary scale on the rod at, say, 2 cm intervals.

Push the rod through holes made in a cardboard box. Make sure you have a tight fit. The distance a vehicle pushes the rod into the box is a measure of the force exerted.

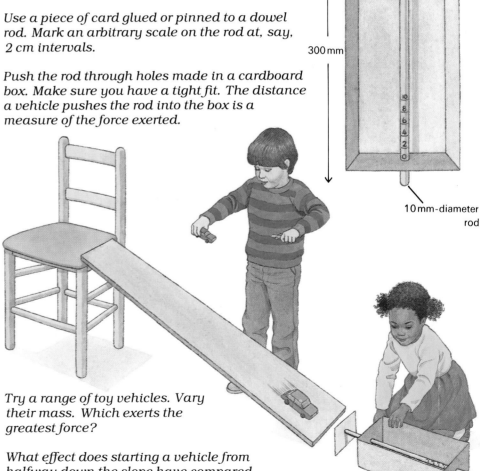

Try a range of toy vehicles. Vary their mass. Which exerts the greatest force?

What effect does starting a vehicle from halfway down the slope have compared with starting from the top of the slope.

Talk about the speed of traffic in your area. Which are the most dangerous roads?

Victorian children spent much of their time learning the alphabet and multiplication tables by heart.

There was great emphasis on calligraphy, practised initially on slates where letters and words were repeated over and over again, and where mistakes could easily be rectified with a wet finger.

Older children wrote with quill pens. A blotted copybook was a serious offence and could result in caning. Such 'correction' was recorded in a punishment book. The headteacher also kept a log book of events.

Once a year, Her Majesty's Inspector of Schools visited to test the children in reading, writing, arithmetic and singing. This visit was a crucial event for school finances, as payment was by results.

Make a display of Victorian classroom artefacts

Make a quill pen

You will need strong wing feathers, preferably from a turkey or goose.

1 *Strip off the barbs with a craft knife. Cut off the bottom of the shaft.*

2 *Cut out a nib shape about 15 to 20 mm from the bottom of the shaft.*

from below

side view

3 *Slope the sides of the nib, then make a 5 mm slit at the end of the shaft.*

from below

side view

4 *Trim the end of the shaft at an angle.*

5 *Try signing your name.*

Make a slate

Use a house roofing slate and a small stone with a sharp edge to scratch on it.

Experiment with other markers. For example, try nail files, nails and coins.

Make a log book

This was usually kept in a ruled book. A Victorian entry might show:

20th June — Average for week 252 Roll 316
Percentage 79·7
There are 28 children absent on doctor's certificates for the following diseases
Scarlet fever — 6
Whooping cough — 9
Mumps — 4
Ringworm — 3
Chicken pox — 3
Excluded — 3

25th June — John Beasley a scholar in Class II Infants has contracted scarlet fever. His brother Henry in attendance at school is excluded for quarantine.

What can the children devise as a modern equivalent?

20th June — Visited the Tower of London Travelled by Hydrofoil from Greenwich to Tower Pier. Mary Twist was sick.

25th June — Yo Yo demonstration in the hall by a lady from the Philippines. Julia Vir Singh was school champion. Children wrote about it afterwards on the word processor.

List all the people who help in the school. Include teachers, dinner helpers, cleaners, caretaker, secretary, school helpers etc.

Take a photograph or do a painting of each person.

Make a display.

Headteacher
Mrs Pottle

Secretary
Mrs Kincaid

Staff
Mrs Beyon

Staff
Miss Clarke

Staff
Mrs Mallett

Staff
Mrs Updyke

Staff
Ms Jones

Staff
Mr Dick

Helper
Mrs Smith

Cook
Mrs Picklet

Assistant cook
Mrs Hickson

Assistant cook
Mrs Moore

Helper
Miss Salt

Caretaker
Mr Black

Cleaner
Mrs Palmer

Cleaner
Miss Todd

Lollipop attendant
Mrs Barnet

How many ways can you group them?

Dinner helpers

How is the dining room arranged? Make a plan. Use templates like those on page 12.

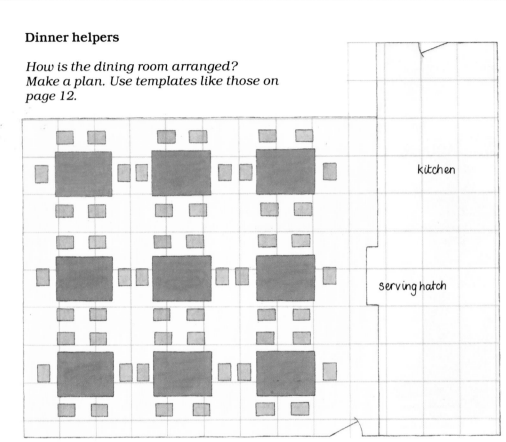
kitchen

serving hatch

Move the templates around to find out if you can create a better layout.

Make up a questionnaire for the dinner helpers.

When do you start?
When do you finish?

What special clothes do you wear?

How is the food kept warm?

Who plans the menus?

Where does the food come from?

Which is the most difficult meal to prepare?

Which is the easiest?

Caretaker

Ask the caretaker to take some of the children into the school's inner sanctum: the boiler room, the store etc.

Get the caretaker to talk about the school heating system. Trace the heating system through the school to your classroom. Mark it on a plan of the school.

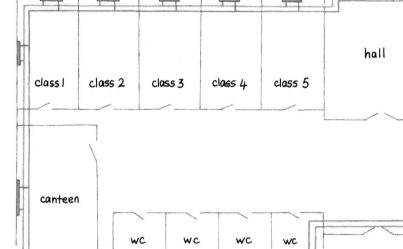

Make a list of what the caretaker has to do.

What were schools like in the past?

Interview people who work in the school and who are over fifty. Tape-record their reminiscences.

How were the classrooms arranged?
What lessons did they have?
What books did they read?
Did they go on visits?
Were they at school during World War II?
What were their favourite games?

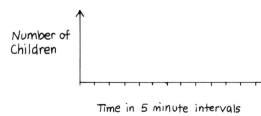

Secretary

Interview the secretary. Make a list of all his or her tasks.

Collecting dinner money
Typing
Receiving visitors
Organising school trips
Taking care of the school fund – banking etc.
Answering parents' queries
Taking phone calls
Photocopying
Other

Find out his or her favourite and least favourite tasks. Examine the dinner-money records and add up the money for the week.

Lollipop attendant

Interview the lollipop attendant. Find out:
when work begins and ends
where the uniform comes from
where the 'lollipop' is kept
whether records are kept or reports are made.

Get a small group of children to record how many children use the crossing point in five minute intervals.

Plot a graph of the results.

Number of
Children

Time in 5 minute intervals

Compare a wet day with a dry day. Is there any difference in the results? Why?

The world is full of sound.

Tape-record those around the school:
  general classroom noise
  singing in the hall
  kitchen staff at work
  a telephone ringing
  a typewriter in action
  chalk on a blackboard
  children at play
  a toilet flushing
  a running tap.

Listen for characteristic, but often ignored, sounds:
  plumbing
  lighting
  heating system
  rain
  wind
  breathing

Look for a pattern in all the sounds. In every case there will be a <u>vibration</u> of some kind producing the sound.

Play a listening game

Divide the class into four groups each with one specific listening task.

Complete a table like the one below.

Group 1 – Sounds made by the children	Group 2 – other sounds in the room
Group 3 – sounds in the rest of the building	Group 4 – sounds outside the building

Discuss the sounds of different happenings

Walk with leather-soled shoes, and then with plimsolls, around a 'listening' class.

Walk with a rustling dress around a 'listening' class.

Pass a sheet of A4 paper as quietly as possible around a 'listening' class.

Record a long continuous note from a recorder or flute. Ask the class to face away from the tape recorder. Play back the sound, turning the volume down as you do so.

Ask the children to put their hands up when they fail to hear the sound. Which parts of the room lose the sound first? Let the children change places to check if this is always so.

Which travels fastest: the sight of an action or the sound of that action?

What are the most distant noises that you can hear?

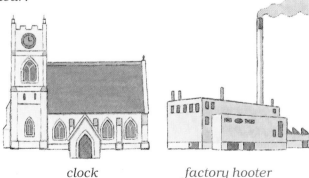

clock   factory hooter

railway

Does the weather have an effect on how well sound travels?

Which travels farthest: a high note, a middle note or a low note?

Let one child walk through the school playing a recorder. The rest of the class remains in the classroom to try to judge where the sound comes from.

Can the class work out the route taken?

What is the speed of sound?

Find a wall that you can get a good echo from.

Bang two wooden blocks together to give the sound for the echo. When you hear the echo, bang the blocks together again.

Time a number of echoes over a measured distance.

$$\text{speed of sound} = \frac{\text{distance travelled}}{\text{time taken}}$$

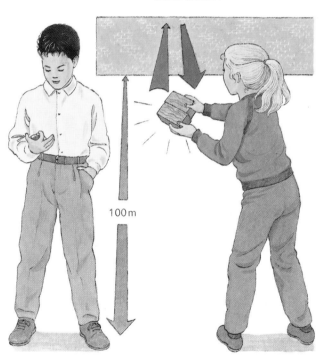

100 m

For example, if you get 50 echoes in 30 seconds when you stand 100 metres from the wall:

$$\text{speed of sound} = \frac{50 \times 200 \text{ metres}}{30 \text{ seconds}}$$
$$= 333 \text{ metres per second}$$

The speed of sound in air is about 330 metres per second.

Survey the homes around the school

Look at the different types and their distribution.

Make drawings and sketches. Encourage children to put in as much detail as they can.

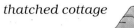

thatched cottage

Georgian terrace

Victorian terrace – second half of the 19th century, working class

Victorian terrace – second half of the 19th century, middle class, multistorey

1920s semi-detached

1930s semi-detached

1960s semi-detached

1960s detached

1970s high-rise flats

Looking at a typical local house

Make sketches and plans. Talk about the services to the house. Make simple sketches to show the layout of rooms and furniture.

This is a typical Victorian terraced house.

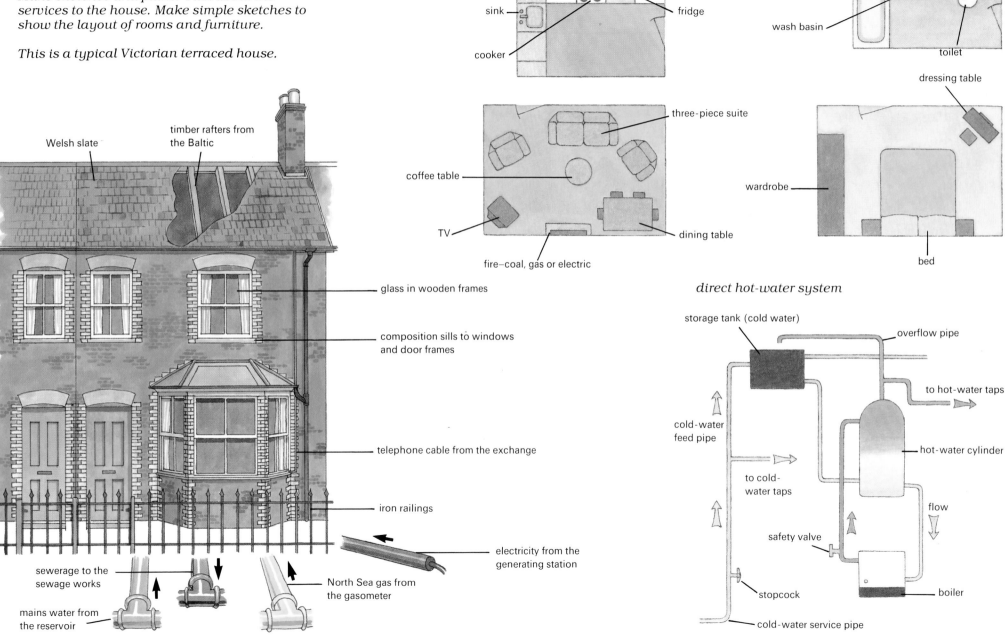

washing machine

sink

cooker

fridge

bath

wash basin

toilet

dressing table

three-piece suite

coffee table

TV

fire–coal, gas or electric

dining table

wardrobe

bed

Welsh slate

timber rafters from the Baltic

glass in wooden frames

composition sills to windows and door frames

telephone cable from the exchange

iron railings

sewerage to the sewage works

North Sea gas from the gasometer

mains water from the reservoir

electricity from the generating station

direct hot-water system

storage tank (cold water)

overflow pipe

cold-water feed pipe

to hot-water taps

to cold-water taps

hot-water cylinder

flow

safety valve

stopcock

boiler

cold-water service pipe

Investigate the different parts of houses in more detail. Make some more sketches.

Look at roofs

Record the different types.

front view   side view

flat roof

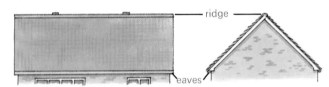
ridge

eaves

plain pitch (is it a low or a high pitch?)

hip

hipped roof

mansard roof

parapet

roof with parapets

Look at roof coverings

slates

ridge tile

plain tiles

double Roman tiles

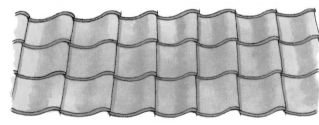

pantiles

corrugated iron

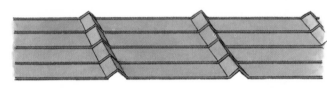

concrete tiles

Street – Hansfield Avenue	
Type of roof	Number
flat	
plain pitch	
hipped	
mansard	

Roof covering	Number
slate	
clay tiles	
concrete tiles	
thatched	
corrugated iron	
other	

Look at doors

There is an enormous variety of doors.

Sketches will reveal the ones common to an area, and to a period. Churches often reveal older styles.

Norman   *old cottage battened door*

However, most doors will be much more modern.

wood-panelled doors   *glass-panelled doors*

Look at windows

Again churches are the best source for older styles.

Norman

There is a wide variety of styles.

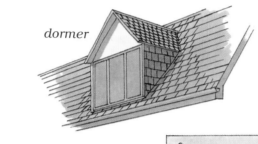

dormer

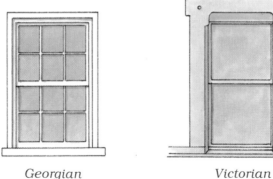

Georgian   *Victorian*

leaded lights

1930s bay window

casement

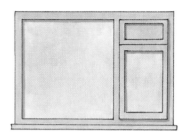

modern

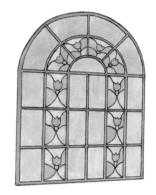

mock-tudor latticework   *stained glass*

Make a 'stained glass' window

Use coloured tissue paper on a classroom window. Try overlapping tissues, Chagall style, to see what effects you get.

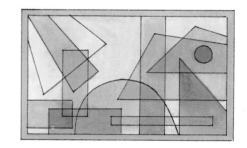

Gather information for a class survey.

What kind of home is it?

Number
of homes

detached semi-detached terrace flat bungalow maisonette other

Are there any chimneys?

Number
of homes

chimneys no chimneys

Is there a garage?

Number
of homes

garage no garage

What kind of windows are there?

Number
of homes

sash windows tip-out windows other

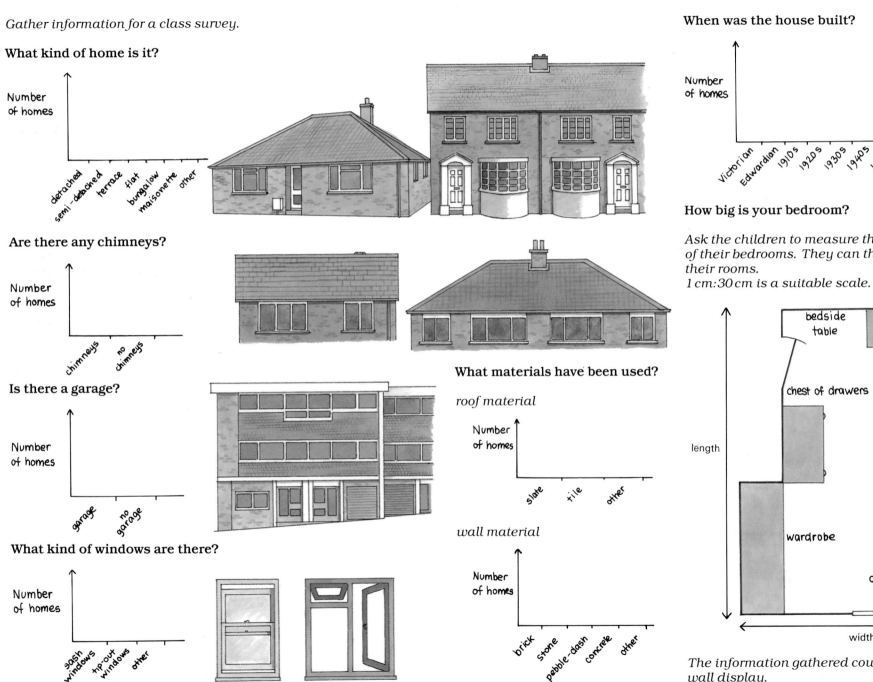

What materials have been used?

roof material

Number
of homes

slate tile other

wall material

Number
of homes

brick stone pebble-dash concrete other

When was the house built?

Number
of homes

Victorian Edwardian 1910s 1920s 1930s 1940s 1950s 1960s 1970s 1980s 1990s

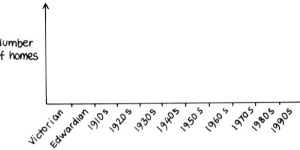

How big is your bedroom?

Ask the children to measure the length and width of their bedrooms. They can then draw plans of their rooms.
1 cm:30 cm is a suitable scale.

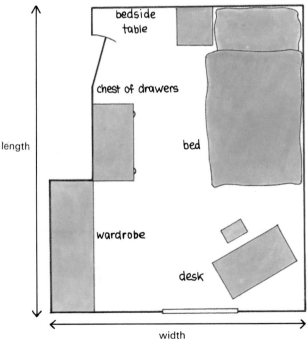

bedside table
chest of drawers
length
bed
wardrobe
desk
width

The information gathered could be set up as a wall display.

What comes into and what goes out of a home?

Ask each child to keep a record for one day. Try to make it as exact as possible. For example, what food, how many newspapers and how much post come in?

You will need very thorough discussion of <u>how to collect</u> the information before you begin.

For example,
Is a questionnaire to be drawn up for parents to fill in?
How will you judge how much water is used?
Will you count how many times the toilet is flushed, how many baths are taken and how many bowls of washing up water are used?
What is the easiest way to keep a tally of phone calls, and so on?

You will also need a thorough discussion of how to tally information across the class and make a display. Breaking down the information and presenting a series of block graphs are an effective way.

Things for recycling/reuse
e.g. newspapers, old clothes, glass

Things the family bring in
e.g. food, clothes, books

Things for the dustbin
e.g. waste food, packaging

Things other people bring in
e.g. newspapers, post, milk

Things that come in pipes or wires
e.g. telephone, water, electricity

Things thrown out for other reasons
e.g. picture which Mum didn't like

Street names

These often give a clue to their origin.

A 'lane' usually means it is an old road.

'Gates' are found in the old parts of cities. They usually signify a break in the city wall.

The main road in a town. An old paved road.

A road leading to a place.

A road named after a battle.

A road named after a family.

A road leading to a river crossing.

Is there one?

Survey the street names in your locality. What conclusions can you draw?

Traffic census

Survey the traffic going into and out of town. You may be able to do this from a school window.

Take a 15 minute period first thing in the morning and again towards the end of the school day. Keep separate records for each side of the road.

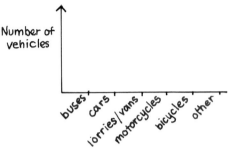

Number of passengers

Survey just the cars over a 15 minute period. How many passengers does each car carry?

Devise a road-safety game

Here is one suggestion to set you thinking.

Make a die. Colour two sides red, three sides green, and one side red and amber.

Take it in turns to throw the die. If you throw
  red: *stop* – **don't move**
  green: *go* – **move two squares**
  red and amber: *prepare to stop, slow down* –
    move one square only.

zebra crossing
stop, not safe to cross
miss a turn

level crossing
no gate, take care
miss a turn

lollipop attendant
pass safely
take an extra turn

school sign flashing amber
cars slowing, but still take care
miss a turn

slip and break a leg
go to hospital
out of game

road works
take care
miss a turn

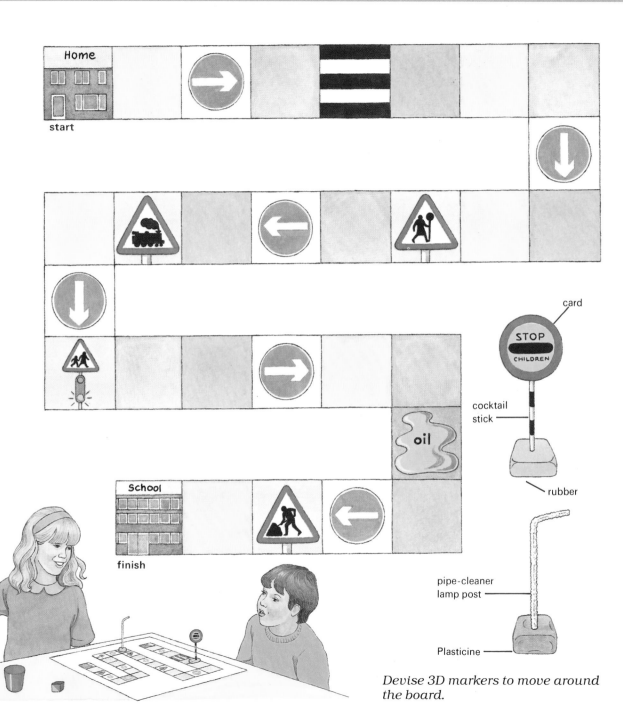

Devise 3D markers to move around the board.

Traffic-light sequences

Watch a traffic light as the colours change.

Show the five different stages on a chart.

Now use a stopwatch to time the colours through the same changes.

Time in each state					
position of lights					
outside school					
main road junction					
near shops					

Do other lights follow the same sequence? Do they take the same time to go through their sequence?

Traffic-junction census

Set four children at a road junction. One at each corner.

Ask each child to count the vehicles <u>approaching</u> the junction along his or her <u>one road</u> for 30 minutes. Add all four results <u>together</u> to give the total volume of traffic passing through the junction in a half-hour period.

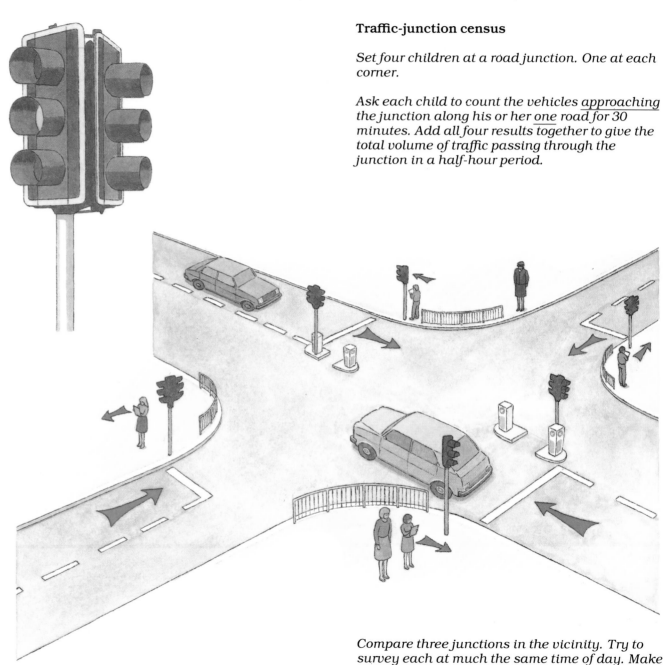

Compare three junctions in the vicinity. Try to survey each at much the same time of day. Make sure you include a busy road junction and a quiet road junction in your survey.

Make some model traffic lights

Wiring model traffic lights is a complex task for many children. Here is a simple working model that most children can easily make and understand.

You will need:

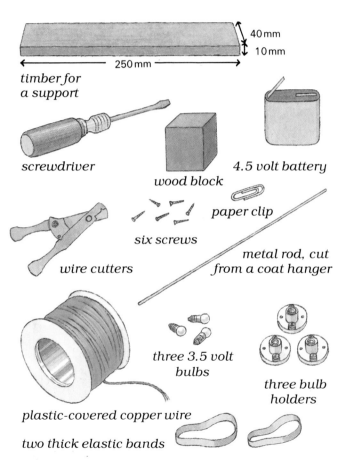

timber for a support

40 mm

10 mm

250 mm

screwdriver

wood block

4.5 volt battery

six screws

paper clip

wire cutters

metal rod, cut from a coat hanger

three 3.5 volt bulbs

three bulb holders

plastic-covered copper wire

two thick elastic bands

1 *Screw the three bulb holders to the piece of timber.*

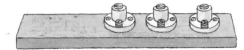

2 *Wire down one side from bulb to bulb.*

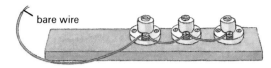

bare wire

3 *Fix the timber upright to the wood block. Use stout elastic bands (or screws).*

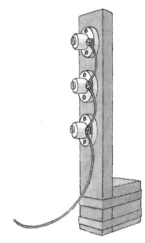

4 *Use painted bulbs or cover them with appropriately coloured cellophane (for example, sweet wrappers). Then connect the battery.*

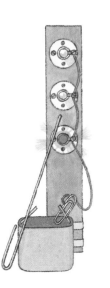

5 *Bend the metal rod like this.*

Use it to make connections from the battery to the bulbs.

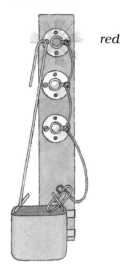

red

red and amber

green

amber

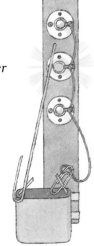

Make a survey of traffic signs

Look at the different types of road signs. Observe how different shapes and colours are used.

This page shows some of the most widely used signs. A comprehensive explanation and listing of road signs is given in the booklet 'Know your Traffic Signs', which is published by HMSO, price £1.20.

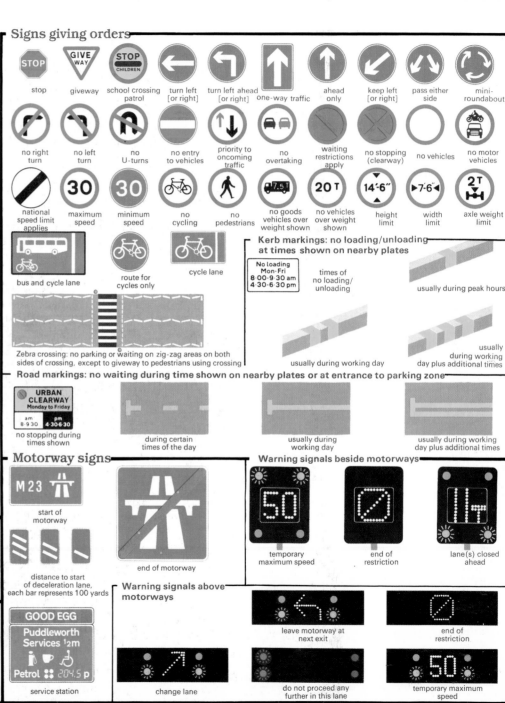

Signs giving orders

stop · giveway · school crossing patrol · turn left [or right] · turn left ahead [or right] · one-way traffic · ahead only · keep left [or right] · pass either side · mini-roundabout

no right turn · no left turn · no U-turns · no entry to vehicles · priority to oncoming traffic · no overtaking · waiting restrictions apply · no stopping (clearway) · no vehicles · no motor vehicles

national speed limit applies · maximum speed · minimum speed · no cycling · no pedestrians · no goods vehicles over weight shown · no vehicles over weight shown · height limit · width limit · axle weight limit

bus and cycle lane · route for cycles only · cycle lane

Kerb markings: no loading/unloading at times shown on nearby plates

No loading Mon-Fri 8·00-9·30 am 4·30-6·30 pm — times of no loading/unloading · usually during peak hours · usually during working day · usually during working day plus additional times

Zebra crossing: no parking or waiting on zig-zag areas on both sides of crossing, except to giveway to pedestrians using crossing

Road markings: no waiting during time shown on nearby plates or at entrance to parking zone

URBAN CLEARWAY Monday to Friday am 8·9·30 pm 4·30·6·30 — no stopping during times shown · during certain times of the day · usually during working day · usually during working day plus additional times

Warning signs

steep hill up · steep hill down · two-way traffic across one-way road · two-way traffic ahead · road narrows on both sides · traffic merges from left · traffic merges from right · dual-carriageway ends · road narrows on right [or left]

road works ahead · loose chippings · road hump ahead · uneven road · hump bridge · bend to right [or left] · staggered junction · round-about · double bend

tunnel · cattle · opening or swing bridge · quayside or river bank · risk of falling rocks · low-flying aircraft · level crossing with barrier · level crossing without barrier · pedestrian crossing

height limit ahead · slippery road · horses crossing · distance to giveway line (GIVE WAY 50 yds) · distance to stop line (STOP 100 yds) · hazard · Fallen tree · School · children going to/from school · NO ROAD MARKINGS FOR 2 MILES worded warning · sharp bend to left [or right]

Information signs

one-way street · no through road · priority over oncoming traffic · hospital · route recommended for cycles · parking for towed caravans · distance to parking place (P 1 mile) · lane ahead reserved for cycles

Direction signs

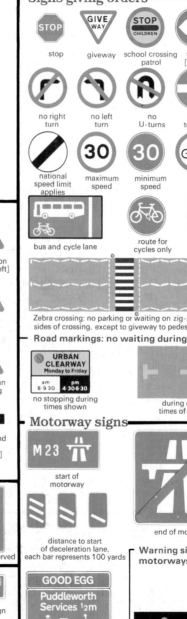

Nottingham A52 25 ½m — used on motorways

Sutton C'field A38 Tamworth (A4091) — used on primary routes

Tavistock Plymouth A38 Exeter A38 — used on local routes

direction to car ferry

pedestrian route to train station

AIR DISPLAY — temporary direction sign

Docks — route for lorries

Motorway signs

M23 — start of motorway

distance to start of deceleration lane, each bar represents 100 yards

end of motorway

GOOD EGG Puddleworth Services ½m Petrol 204.5 p — service station

Warning signals beside motorways

50 temporary maximum speed · end of restriction · lane(s) closed ahead

Warning signals above motorways

leave motorway at next exit · end of restriction · change lane · do not proceed any further in this lane · 50 temporary maximum speed

Make a collection of local signs

Look for signs which give orders and signs which give warnings. Photograph or sketch them.

Draw some of the signs that give local directions.

Design some signs

Imagine that some foreign children are visiting your school. Invent some signs to help them as they move around the school. Bear in mind that they might not be able to read English.

dining room

keep left

boys' toilet

turn left to the library

no running on the stairs

no roller skating

school pond

biting hamster

headteacher's room

Streets can be colourful.

Look at street name signs

These are usually black on white. It this the best combination?

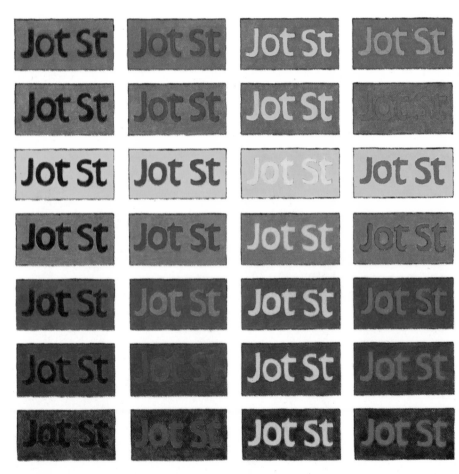

Make up different coloured street names on different coloured backgrounds. Compare painting the signs with cutting out coloured sugar-paper letters on different coloured backgrounds.

Test your signs in the playground. Which show up best?

Shop colours

Look at window displays. A greengrocers is a good start.

Shop	Red	Orange	Yellow	Green	Blue	Brown	Black
greengrocer	apples tomatoes cabbage radishes peppers cherries strawberries redcurrants beetroot chillies	oranges carrots tangerines mandarins peppers clementines	bananas lemons starfruit apricots peaches apples	cabbages lettuce beans grapes apples leeks spring onions avocados spinach courgettes	figs blueberries plums	potatoes dates nuts passion fruit ginger onions swede mushrooms	grapes blackberries aubergine

Collect packages

Look for colour.

Collect labels

Look for colour.

Which cars show up best?

Survey cars at a distance. Judge
which show up best. Invent a
scoring system:
    shows up well – 3
    shows up reasonably – 2
    shows up poorly – 1.

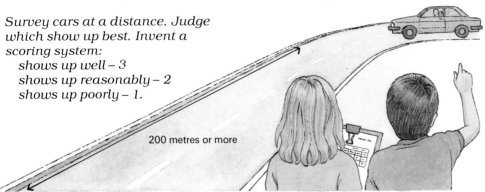

200 metres or more

Name	Sunny day					Cloudy day				
	Red	White	Black	Brown	Other	Red	White	Black	Brown	Other

Make up a test using toy cars

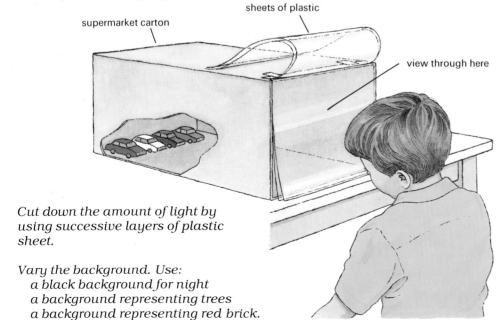

sheets of plastic

supermarket carton

view through here

Cut down the amount of light by
using successive layers of plastic
sheet.

Vary the background. Use:
    a black background for night
    a background representing trees
    a background representing red brick.

Which is the safest colour to wear?

Compare the orange arm bands used for road
safety with home-made bands.

safety pin

Use brightly coloured sticky paper stuck to card
bands. Use a safety pin to hold each one in place.

Try them out in the playground. How does
distance affect the results? Is the same colour the
best in the early morning, during the day and at
dusk?

How is colour used in the street?

What sorts of things are red?
What sorts of things are yellow?
What other colours are used?

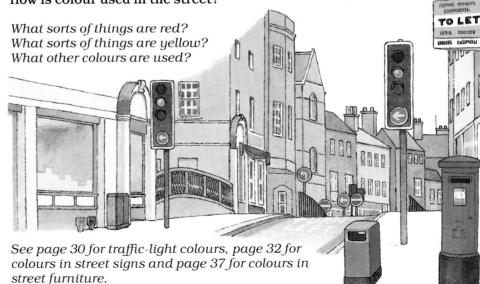

TO LET

See page 30 for traffic-light colours, page 32 for
colours in street signs and page 37 for colours in
street furniture.

Look at the structure of the local streets.

Drain covers

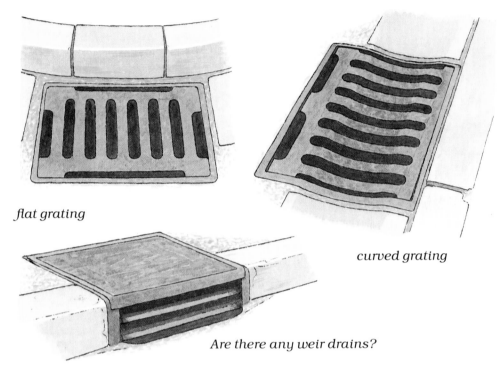

flat grating

curved grating

Are there any weir drains?

Look through a drain cover into the gully pot.
Take care! In cross-section it looks like this.

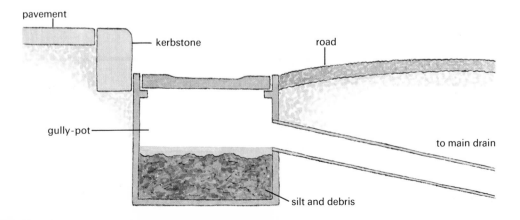

pavement

kerbstone

road

gully-pot

to main drain

silt and debris

Kerbstones

What kind of kerbstones are there?

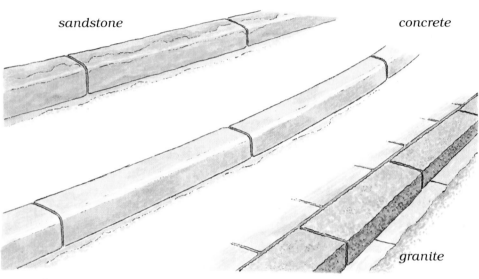

sandstone

concrete

granite

Holes in the road

Look at the structure of a road which is under repair.

bitumen road

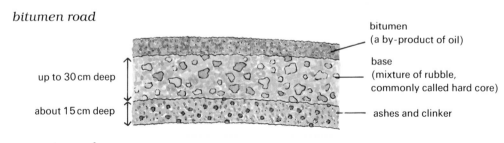

up to 30 cm deep

about 15 cm deep

bitumen
(a by-product of oil)

base
(mixture of rubble,
commonly called hard core)

ashes and clinker

concrete road

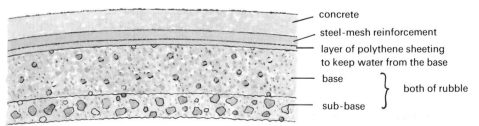

concrete

steel-mesh reinforcement

layer of polythene sheeting
to keep water from the base

base

both of rubble

sub-base

Make sketches of street furniture.

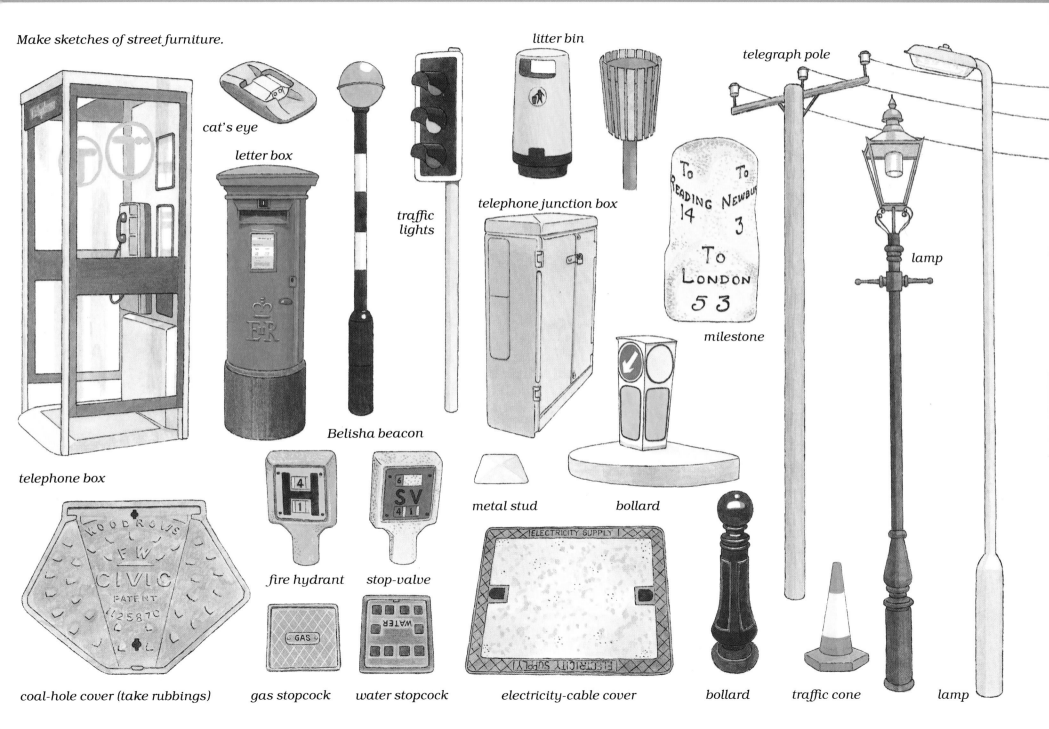

litter bin

telegraph pole

cat's eye

letter box

traffic
lights

telephone junction box

To   To
READING   NEWBUR
14   3

TO
LONDON
5 3

milestone

lamp

Belisha beacon

telephone box

metal stud   bollard

fire hydrant   stop-valve

coal-hole cover (take rubbings)   gas stopcock   water stopcock   electricity-cable cover   bollard   traffic cone   lamp

Lamp posts

There are three sizes of lamp post: 5, 10 and 13 metres, with powers of 35, 135 and 180 watts, respectively.

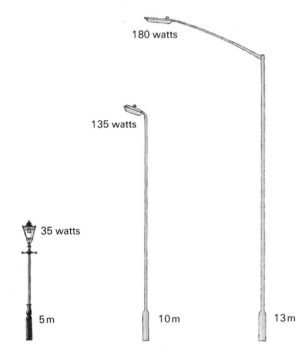

180 watts

135 watts

35 watts

5 m   10 m   13 m

In town shopping areas the largest posts may have lamps with a power of 250 watts.

On top of each lamp there is a small dome.

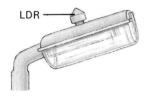

LDR

The dome contains a light-dependent resistor or LDR. It controls when the lamp comes on and goes off. At light intensities of 70 lux it switches the lamp on and at 100 lux it switches the lamp off.

Make a survey

1 Make sketches of the lamp posts. Label the LDR.
2 Measure the position of the lamp in relation to the kerb. Take care. (In each case, the outreach arm of the lamp post should place the lamp over the kerb.)
3 Measure the distance between lamp posts in a quiet residential street.
   Measure the distance between lamp posts on a busy road.
   How do they differ?

Lighting plan

Design a brief for street lighting in two contrasting streets near to the school. Consider:
the type and amount of traffic in the streets
the state and type of road surface
the light level needed
the uses of the streets in order to decide:
    the kind of lamp post
    its height
    its wattage
    the space between posts.

Colour

Discuss the colour of street lighting and how it affects the colour of things.

Zebra crossing lights (Belisha beacons)

Do the two lights flash in or out of sync?

Time the flashes over one minute. Is the number the same for all Belisha beacons?

Stability

Kelly doll

Traffic cones are designed for stability. Like a Kelly doll they have a low centre of gravity. They also have a wide base.

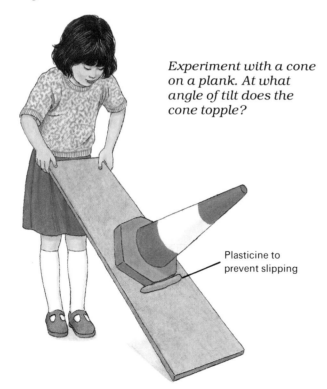

Experiment with a cone on a plank. At what angle of tilt does the cone topple?

Plasticine to prevent slipping

Design some traffic cones

Make cones from card or from the sides of discarded supermarket cartons.

Test your cones out. Experiment with:
   the size of the base
   the height of the cone
   the heaviness of the base.

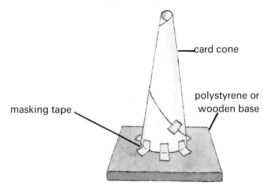

card cone

polystyrene or wooden base

masking tape

Make them in different colours.

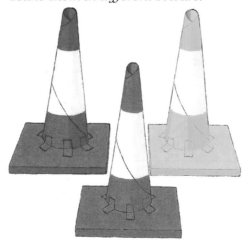

Which cones show up best at a distance? Test them on a dull day and a bright day. Do you get the same results?

Make a sketch of a row of shops. Look carefully for the different kinds of stone that are used.

Look for marble

Marble is usually white, grey, pink, black or green. There are no grains or crystals to be seen. The stone is smooth and polished.

Look for limestone

Limestone is a very fine-grained rock, which is pale grey or yellow.

Look for granite

Granite is speckled and glistening. It comes in black with white, grey, brown or pink flecks.

Any others?

Also look for concrete, tiles, slates and bricks.

Keep a record.

Stone spotted	Natural or artificial	Colour	Where spotted	Use
marble	natural	pink	Lloyds Bank	walls
concrete	artificial	grey	chemist	lintels

Let the children sketch a shop that interests them.

Make a row of model shops

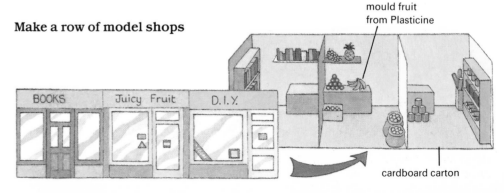

Customer survey

Survey a small number of shops for ten minutes.

How many people enter each shop during the survey?

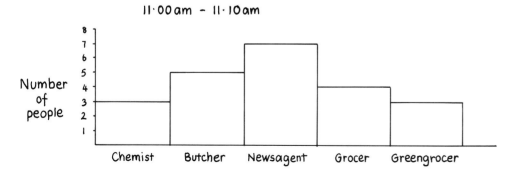

11·00am – 11·10am

Number of people

Chemist   Butcher   Newsagent   Grocer   Greengrocer

Make the survey at different times through the day. When are peak shopping times for each shop?

Street directories

The archives for your borough, or the borough reference library, will usually have old street directories. These will list the use of shops.

Record their changing use.

Address : 50 Albany Road		
Dates	Occupant	Use
1851 – 1855	William Short	grocer
1855 – 1858	George King	greengrocer
1858 – 1874	George Smith	greengrocer
1874 – 1878	John Soper	greengrocer
1878 – 1881	Henry Rawlings	butcher
1881 – 1882	George Hutchinson	butcher
1882 – 1897	Sarah Morley	art, needlework
1901 – 1905	Rawlings Bros.	electrical engineers
1905 – 1912	Simon and Patterson	blouses and shirts
1916 – 1921	E.R. Rayner	print seller and picture restorer
1921 – 1940	M. Boydell	gowns and knitwear
1940 – 1956	Stephen Riddington	poster and signboard company
1956 –	E. Minassian	oriental carpets

Plot the general distribution of shops in the area.

Use a large-scale local map. Mark corner shops in red, and main shopping parades in blue. Large supermarkets can be singled out in another colour, as can local markets. Make a key.

What observations can you make on the general distribution of shops? What is the nature of the business in corner shops? What access is there to the shops?

Make a detailed list of local facilities

Here is a sample survey chart. You can add to it.

Key

house	
corner shop	
main shop	
supermarket	
market	

Shop	Number	Shop	Number
antiques		grocery	
baker		hairdresser	
bank		hardware	
builders merchant		ironmonger	
butcher		linen draper	
café		optician	
card shop		pets	
chain store		post office	
charity shop		records	
clothes		sewing machines	
cobbler		shoes	
decorator		socks	
DIY		supermarket	
electrical		take away	
estate agent		television	
fancy goods		ties	
fishing tackle		video	
fishmonger		wools	
furniture		other	

Look for signs

Make records of local shop and public-house signs. Make drawings or take photographs.

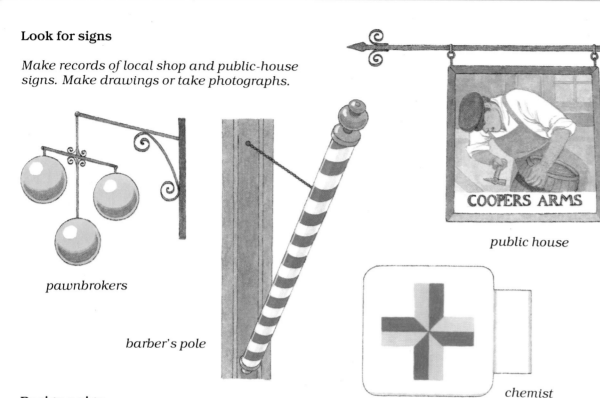

pawnbrokers

barber's pole

public house

chemist

Design a sign

Design your own shop signs for the local shops.

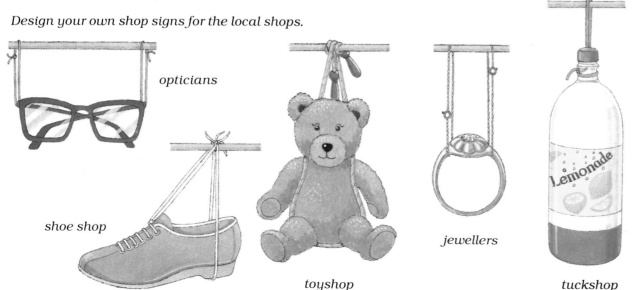

opticians

shoe shop

toyshop

jewellers

tuckshop

Lettering

Examine the different kinds of lettering found on local shop fronts.

Make a rough estimate of the length and height of each section of lettering in order to make copies of approximately the right proportions.

Clarence Hotel

JOHNSONS
GALLERIES

JANE'S
INTERIORS

The CAVE Wine Bar

SIAN'S
RESTAURANT

Sandra's
Unisex Hairdressers

ERIC'S greengrocer

Practise different styles of lettering. Make up some shop titles of your own.

Cloud cover

Cloud cover is estimated in eighths.

 symbol for clear sky

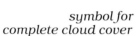 *symbol for complete cloud cover*

You might ask why weather forecasters use eighths. However, if you try measuring cloud cover in smaller units such as tenths, it becomes difficult to judge.

The symbols for the different amounts of cloud cover are shown below.

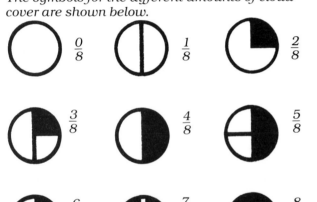

$\frac{0}{8}$ $\frac{1}{8}$ $\frac{2}{8}$

$\frac{3}{8}$ $\frac{4}{8}$ $\frac{5}{8}$

$\frac{6}{8}$ $\frac{7}{8}$ $\frac{8}{8}$

Keep a daily record

Look for links between cloud cover and other weather such as rain, storms, showers and sunshine.

Date	Time	Cloud cover	Comments on weather

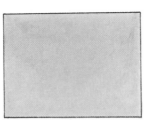

$\frac{0}{8}$

$\frac{2}{8}$

$\frac{4}{8}$

$\frac{6}{8}$

$\frac{7}{8}$

Cloud shapes

Draw and paint some of the various cloud shapes:
<u>cumulus clouds</u> are cauliflower shaped
<u>nimbus clouds</u> are dark, threatening rain clouds
<u>cirrus clouds</u> are thin wispy clouds which are usually found high in the sky.

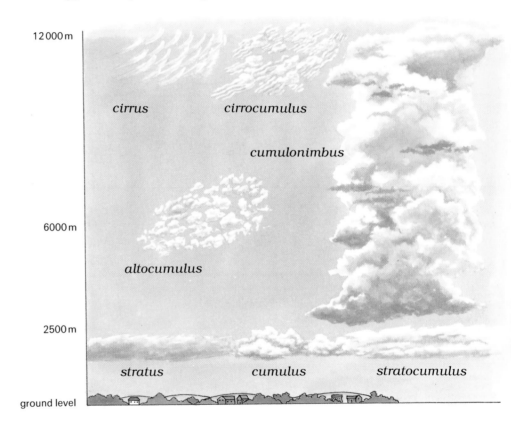

Record their height on a daily basis.

Keep records of your observations.

Date	Time	Shape	Colour	Height	Description

Cumulus
(cauliflower shaped)

Stratocumulus
(develops rolls or rounded masses)

Stratus
(featureless grey cloud)

Altocumulus

Altocumulus floccus

Cirrus
(mares' tails)

Cirrocumulus

Cumulonimbus

Make a rain gauge

The receiving bottle must have a smaller diameter than the funnel or it will not fit inside the drainpipe. Therefore, calibrate the receiving bottle so that the height of the water inside it relates directly to the surface area of the funnel.

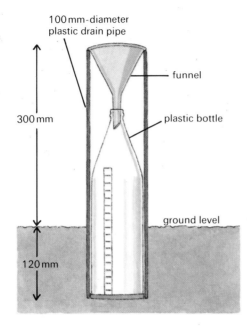

100 mm-diameter plastic drain pipe

funnel

plastic bottle

300 mm

120 mm

ground level

The easiest method of calibration is to pour water into the receiving bottle from a bottle of the *same diameter* as the funnel. Add a measured depth of water each time and mark the scale up the side of the bottle in millimetres.

Set up a rain gauge. Position it so that it receives direct rainfall, and no splashes from walls and so on.

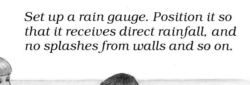

Make a sunshine recorder

You will need a large deep tin, with a well fitting lid.

Make a pin-prick sized hole in the lid of the tin. Line the inside with light-sensitive paper.

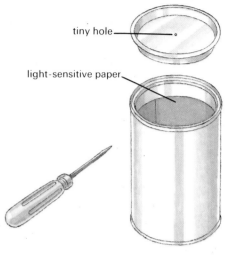

tiny hole

light-sensitive paper

Place the tin where the sun can shine continually through the hole during the day. Change the paper at the end of each day. Mount the results for the week.

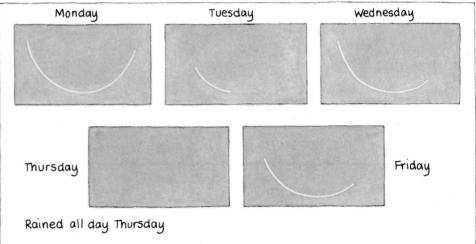

Monday	Tuesday	Wednesday
Thursday	Friday	

Rained all day Thursday

What does the record show about the sun's movements relative to the earth? How do the results relate to the cloud-cover record?

Make a wind vane

Set up a wind vane to find wind direction.

A ball-point pen cap balanced on a steel knitting needle makes a good base on which to stick the card vane.

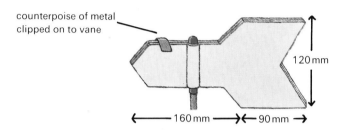

counterpoise of metal clipped on to vane

120 mm

◀━ 160 mm ━▶◀ 90 mm ▶

The wind exerts a turning effect on the broad tail. It is necessary to have a balancing weight to counteract the heaviness of the tail. Once the balance is right, the vane will spin easily.

The vane always points to the direction the wind is coming <u>from</u>. Use a compass to establish north.

Keep records.

Date	Wind direction

Make a wind-sock

You can also find the wind direction with a wind-sock.

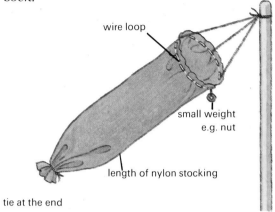

wire loop

small weight e.g. nut

length of nylon stocking

tie at the end

The top half of a nylon stocking held open with a loop of wire makes a good wind-sock. Fix the three strings at equal distances apart on the wire loop and attach their other ends to a stake.

Position the stake away from buildings to avoid wind eddies.

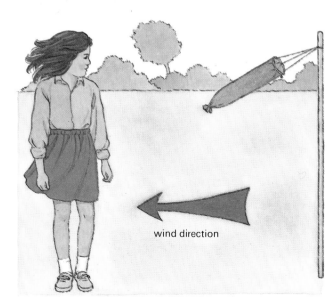

wind direction

Look for weather vanes

Look for local examples. Make drawings of them or take photographs.

Rotating anemometer

Wind speed is usually measured with an anemometer.

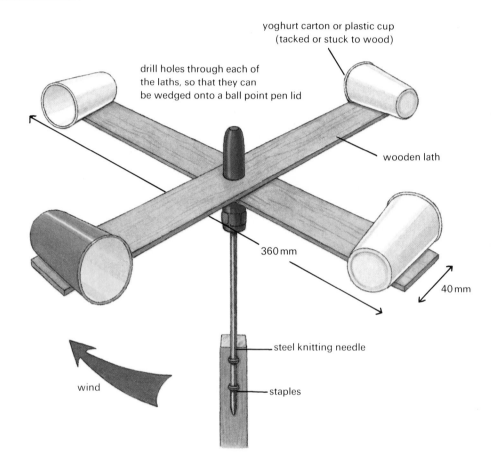

yoghurt carton or plastic cup (tacked or stuck to wood)

drill holes through each of the laths, so that they can be wedged onto a ball point pen lid

wooden lath

360 mm

40 mm

steel knitting needle

staples

wind

The anemometer shown is fun for children to make. Count the number of revolutions per minute. Colour one of the cartons to facilitate this.

Compare wind speed from day to day.

This type of anemometer becomes difficult to use if the wind gets up since the arms spin too quickly to count the number of revolutions.

Flap anemometer

This anemometer is reputed to have been devised by Leonardo da Vinci. It has a hanging flap rather like an inn sign. The wind blows the flap out at an angle.

This angle tends to be rather unsteady, so decide whether to take maximum readings or to go for an average.

An arbitrary scale can be built up if you take readings in different wind conditions.

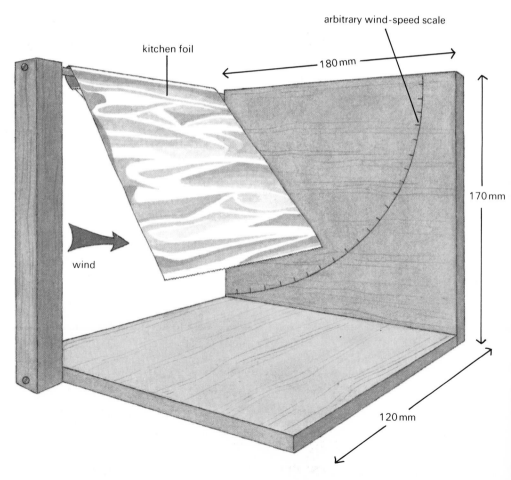

arbitrary wind-speed scale

kitchen foil

180 mm

170 mm

wind

120 mm

The Beaufort scale is an observational method of measuring wind speed developed by Sir Francis Beaufort, a British admiral, for use at sea.

Compare your anemometer readings against this modified scale for children.

Force	Description	Signs on land	speed (mph)
0	calm	calm, smoke rises vertically	less than 1
1	light air	direction of wind shown by smoke drift but not by wind vanes	1–3
2	light breeze	wind felt on face, leaves rustle, vanes move	4–7
3	gentle breeze	leaves and small twigs in constant motion, wind extends light flag	8–12
4	moderate breeze	raises dust and loose paper, smaller branches are moved	13–18
5	fresh breeze	small trees in leaf begin to sway	19–24
6	strong breeze	large branches in motion, whistling in telegraph wires	25–31
7	near gale	whole trees in motion, inconvenience felt when walking against the wind	32–38
8	fresh gale	breaks twigs off trees, impedes progress	39–46

Make your own pictorial version

0 calm	1 light air	2 light breeze
3 gentle breeze	4 moderate breeze	5 fresh breeze
6 strong breeze	7 near gale	8 fresh gale

Temperature

Use an ordinary wall thermometer to take the temperature.

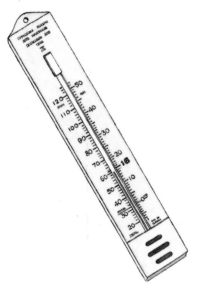

Do this in the shade <u>at the same time</u> each day.

Keep a record.

Date	Temperature

Take the temperature at regular intervals throughout one day.

Time	Temperature
9·00	
10·00	

Use a Six's thermometer to record maximum and minimum temperatures each day.

Again keep a record.

Day	Max.temperature	Min.temperature

Don't forget to reset the thermometer after you've taken your daily reading.

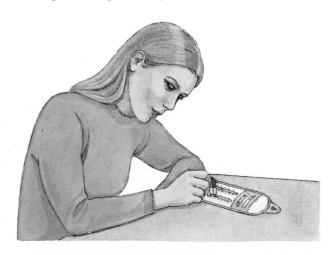

Visibility

Ideally, you need a school with a commanding view of the local area. Alternatively, children living at the top of high-rise blocks of flats could bring information to school on a daily basis.

The following standard boundaries are used for measuring visibility:

2 km ($1\frac{1}{4}$ miles)	20 km ($12\frac{1}{2}$ miles)
4 km ($2\frac{1}{2}$ miles)	30 km ($18\frac{2}{3}$ miles)
7 km ($4\frac{1}{3}$ miles)	40 km (25 miles)
10 km ($6\frac{1}{4}$ miles)	

Use an Ordnance Survey map to identify objects at each of these distances. These objects can then be looked for on a daily basis.

Keep records.

Day	Visibility distance	Comments
Monday	40 km	Clear cloudless sky
Tuesday	20 metres	fog
Wednesday		

Some weather readings need only be taken once a day. First thing in the morning, at say 9 a.m., is often a good time.

Rainfall

Daily

Keep a physical record.

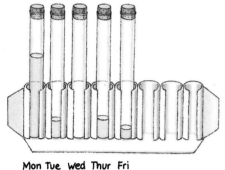

Mon Tue Wed Thur Fri

Weekly

Make a block graph.

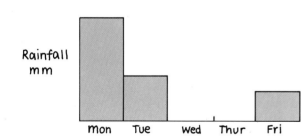

Rainfall mm

mon   Tue   wed   Thur   Fri

Monthly

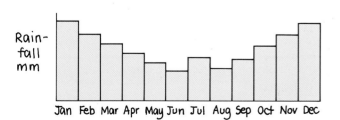

Rainfall mm

Jan Feb Mar Apr May Jun Jul Aug Sep Oct Nov Dec

Temperature

Hourly

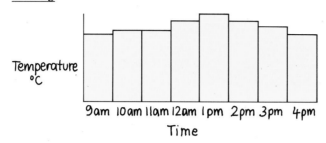

Temperature °C

9am 10am 11am 12am 1pm 2pm 3pm 4pm

Time

Daily

maximum   minimum

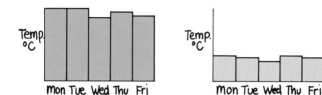

Temp. °C   Temp. °C

Mon Tue Wed Thu Fri   Mon Tue Wed Thu Fri

Monthly

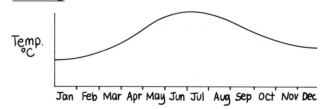

Temp. °C

Jan Feb Mar Apr May Jun Jul Aug Sep Oct Nov Dec

Wind direction

Record this on a daily basis.

April	Wind direction	Comment
1	SW	warm, showery
2	W	warm, showery
3	W	warm, bright intervals

Wind speed

Use your arbitrary scale.
Relate these readings to the Beaufort scale.

Date	Scale reading	Beaufort scale

Weather sayings

Collect weather sayings and judge them against your records.

'The north wind doth blow
And we shall have snow.'

'Red sky at night shepherd's delight
Red sky in the morning sailor's warning.'

'When the dew is on the grass
Rain will never come to pass.'

'When the grass is dry at night
Look for rain before the light.'

'A deep clear sky of feckless hue
Breeds storms within a day or two.'

'Rain before seven clear before eleven.'

'Where grass is dry at morning light
Look for rain before the night.'

'When the wind is in the east
It's good for neither man nor beast.
When the wind is in the north
The old folk should not venture forth.
When the wind is in the south
It blows the bait in the fish's mouth.
When the wind is in the west
It is of all the winds the best.'

1 *Old parish churches grew bit by bit. The earliest churches had just a <u>nave</u> for the congregation and a <u>sanctuary</u> holding the altar.*

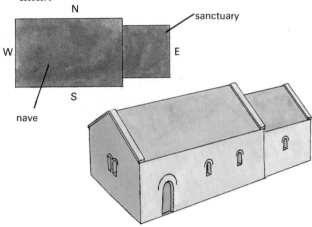

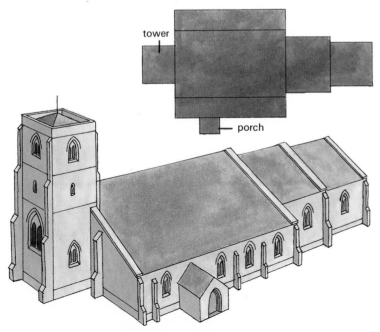

2 *The chancel was then added to the eastern end of the church, between the nave and the sanctuary. The choir stalls are found here.*

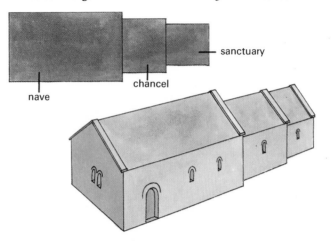

3 *Side pieces, the aisles, came as a later addition, so that the clergy could process to the altar. Often the north aisle was built before the south aisle because the south side of the church contained graves.*

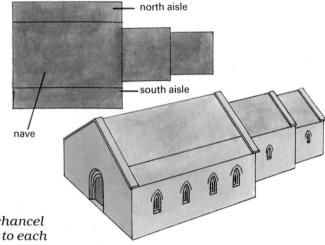

4 *Towers and spires were then added.*

5 *Sometimes the tower is between the chancel and the nave. Transepts were added to each side of the tower. Thus, you get a cruciform church.*

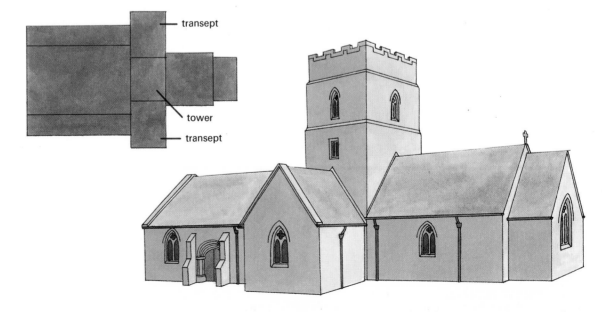

Look at your parish or local church. Identify the main parts. Try and work out how it has evolved.

Draw a plan of the church. Use different colours to shade in the parts which have been added at various times over the centuries.

General survey

Make a class survey of places of worship used by the children.

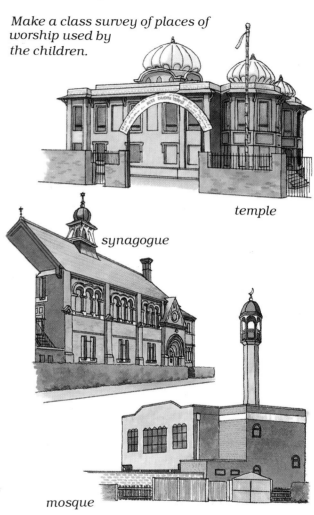

temple

synagogue

mosque

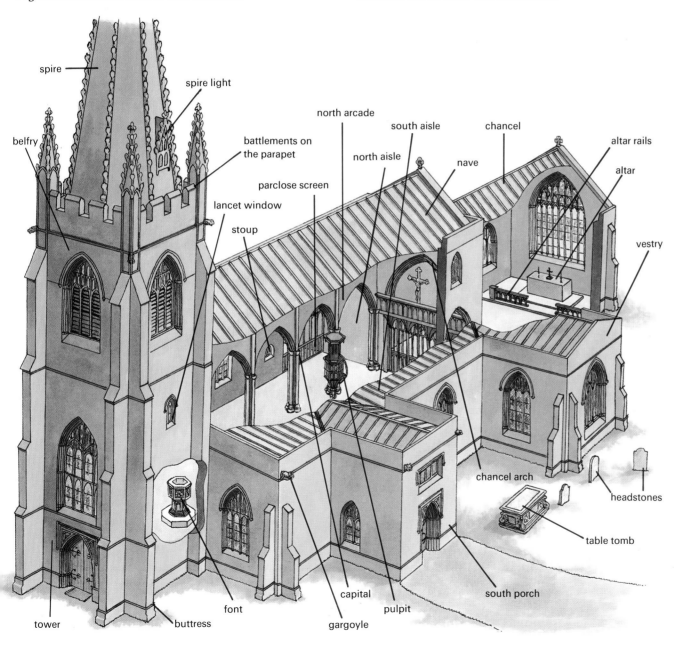

spire

spire light

north arcade

south aisle

chancel

belfry

battlements on the parapet

north aisle

nave

altar rails

parclose screen

altar

lancet window

stoup

vestry

chancel arch

headstones

capital

pulpit

south porch

table tomb

tower

buttress

font

gargoyle

List the various places of worship.

Churches — denominations

Synagogues —

mosques —

temples —

Plot them on a local map. Ask the children to describe the form of ceremony that goes on in each.

Windows give clues to the age of a church.
Make sketches and drawings.

Saxon

Norman

Early English

Decorated

Perpendicular

Tudor

Restoration

Georgian

Regency

Victorian Gothic

Late Victorian

There are lots of other things you can make notes about and sketch.

Capitals *(the top part of the columns)*

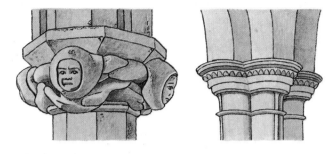

Fonts

Buttresses

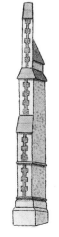

Roofs *(interior)*

king-post roof

common rafters

ridge piece

strut

king post

longitudinal strut

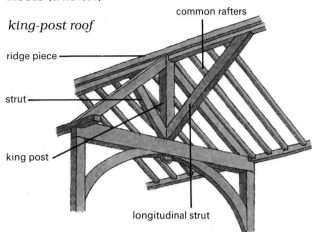

Window decorations

nail head

cable

pellet

lozenge

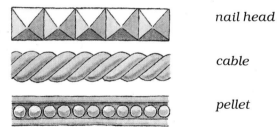

Gargoyles *(water spouts)*

Carved wood

bench ends

roof bosses

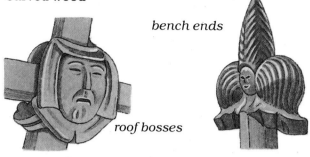

miserichord (under a tip-up seat)

Monumental brasses

The vicar may give permission for you to make rubbings.

Find out about the person represented.

Materials

What materials have been used to build the church? Limestone is common. Red sandstone, granite, chert, flint, brick and other modern materials are also used.

Measure the heights and lengths of some of the blocks used to build the church.

Sample	Length	Height
west front		
porch		

Look for marks made by the mason when cutting the blocks.

marks made by a saw when the block was cut

stone mason's chisel marks

flint shatter mark

Look for the masons' marks. These are cut into the stone to identify individual masons.

Pillars

Make a survey of pillars.

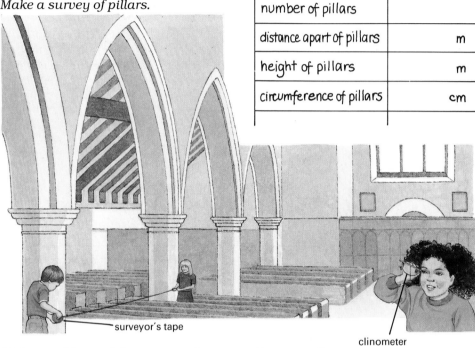

surveyor's tape

clinometer

Make a rubbing of the texture of a stone pillar.

fix with Blu-tack

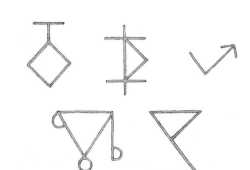

Name of church	Pillar survey
number of pillars	
distance apart of pillars	m
height of pillars	m
circumference of pillars	cm

Draw a pillar.

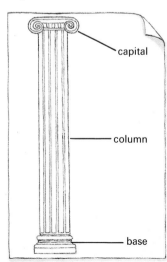

capital

column

base

Is there a churchyard cross?

Are there any special tombs?

Make sketches of them.

What is the oldest grave you can find?
List the common surnames.
Are these surnames still common in the area?
Survey the age at which people died. Victorian graves will contain many more young people compared with contemporary ones.

Here lies Intered Andrew pars ons from London Gen

A J n
Memory of
RICHARD COURT
who died July 31ʰ 1791

Make a record of any interesting epitaphs.

Our book of Epitaphs

Gravestones

Stone is cut, shaped and polished to make gravestones. They come in many colours.

Make a graph to illustrate the most popular colours.

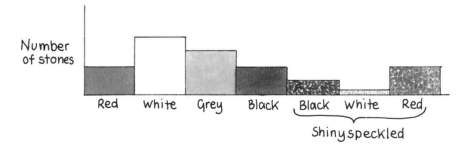

Which colour is the most common?

Compare the graves on the north side of the church with those on the south. Where are the oldest ones?

Is there any building going on in your locality? It might be a few houses being built as an infill in a residential street, a whole estate, offices or factories.

In each case the first person to contact is the site supervisor. Ask whether you can visit and if there are safe places where the children can stand and watch. Ask if you might see the plans. Try to obtain some old plans to show the children.

Make your own plans

The architect will have drawn up the plans.

Plans show what objects look like when you adopt a bird's-eye view of the world and look down on things.

Set up a painting easel as an architect's drawing board.

set square

T-square

Use a T-square and a set-square to draw vertical and horizontal lines, and a pair of compasses to draw circles.

Page 12 shows a plan of the classroom. Make up some other plans of things viewed from above.

snowman

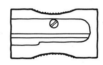

pencil sharpener

closed pair of compasses

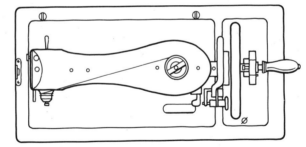

sewing machine

waste-paper basket

cup and saucer

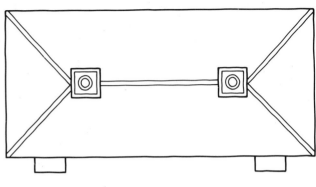

roof with chimneys

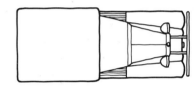

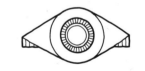

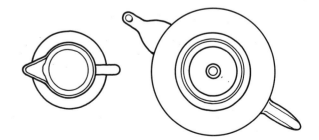

Some of the architect's drawings will show things in elevation and section.

Elevations

Examine some common objects in the classroom. Draw them in elevation, that is so that you can see what they look like from the side.

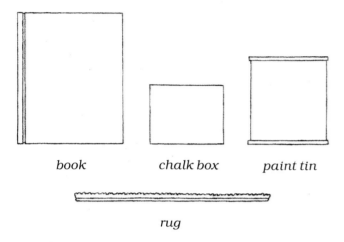

book   chalk box   paint tin

rug

Sections

Now draw them in section. That is as if they had been chopped in two.

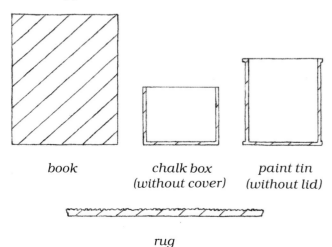

book   chalk box (without cover)   paint tin (without lid)

rug

Tools

Builders need to make sure that walls are vertical and floors are horizontal. There are two ancient and essential tools for this purpose: the plumb bob and the spirit level.

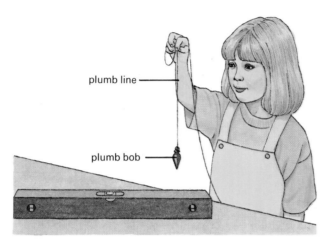

plumb line

plumb bob

Each of these can easily be adapted for use in school, but children will also enjoy looking at the real tools used on the building site.

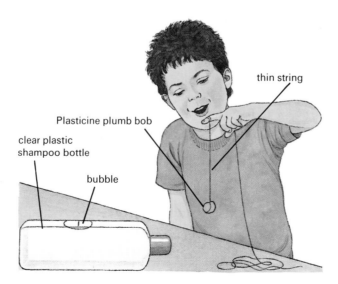

thin string

Plasticine plumb bob

clear plastic shampoo bottle

bubble

Use your improvised tools to check that walls in the school are upright and floors and window sills are level.

Vertical		Horizontal	
Object	Checked	Object	Checked

Use a folded sheet of paper as a tool for checking right angles where walls meet.

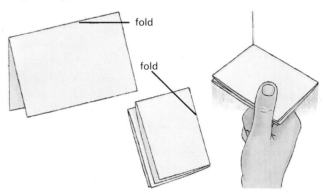

fold

fold

One of the most noticeable things when visiting a building site is the trenches bearing the foundations. Usually these follow the outline of the walls that are to be built.

concrete base

Look for the concrete base at the bottom of the trench. This supports the walls and is wider than them.

Back at school, experiment to find out how this concrete 'raft' works.

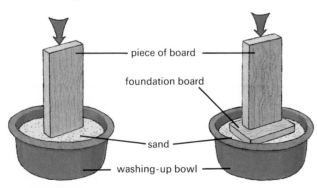

piece of board
foundation board
sand
washing-up bowl

Press the board into sand, with and without a foundation board. When is it easier?

In some developments the builders have to drive in lots of concrete piles.

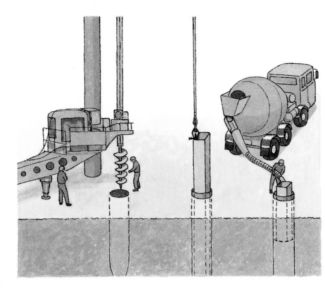

These piles are held by the friction between them and the soil.

Try this for yourself. Hammer some large nails of equal size into a wood block.

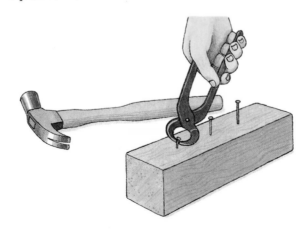

Drive each nail in a different distance. Which is easiest to lever out? Which is hardest?
The deeper the nail, the greater the friction

Try simulating load-bearing piles.

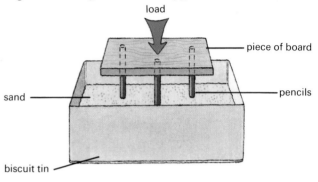

load
piece of board
sand
pencils
biscuit tin

Use more pencils if the foundations are too weak.

Try this on a larger scale.

Take care!

brick
tray
cricket stumps

Will this set up bear a child's weight? Sit a child carefully on the tray. Have other children support the child.

Brick walls are built on concrete foundations. A damp-proof course prevents water rising up through the bricks.

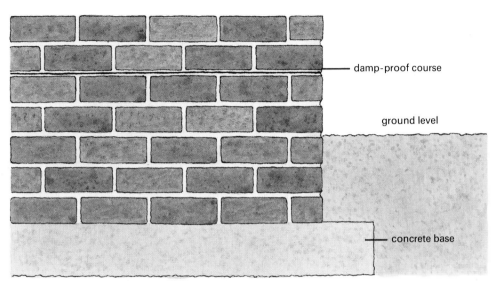

Look at the types of bonding used in the walls. Examine and experiment with different mortar mixes (see 'An Early Start to Technology', page 77).

Look for the cavity between the two external walls of houses. Look for the metal ties which hold the two walls together.

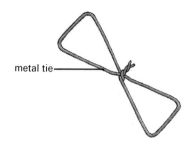

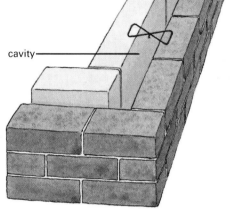

The damp-proof course can be made of slate, sheets of metal such as lead and copper, or felt treated with asphalt or bitumen.

Try out various materials to find out which make good insulators.

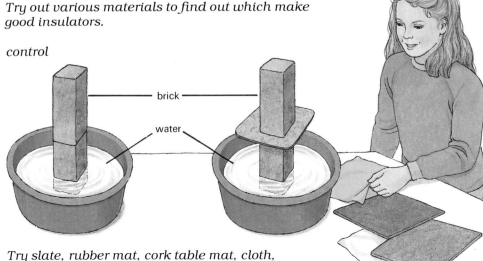

Try slate, rubber mat, cork table mat, cloth, plastic sheet and so on.

The air in this cavity helps both to insulate the house and to stop driving rain penetrating into the home.

Test out the insulating effect of a cavity

Use two tins of the same size and one larger tin.

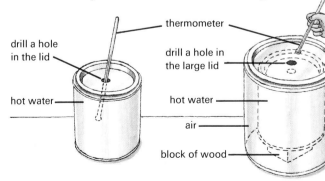

Which water cools more quickly? The water in the tin which is directly in contact with the air, or the water in the tin insulated by a cavity of air.

Sketch the stages in the development of a house. List all the materials used.

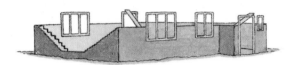

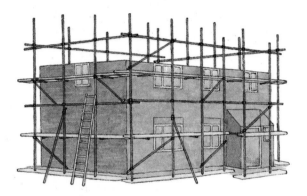

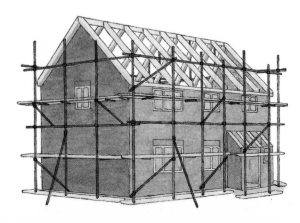

How heavy?

Estimate the number of facing bricks in a house.

Check by counting. Can the children devise quick ways of doing this?

Take one brick back to school. Weigh it. Work out the total mass of bricks used for the facing walls of the house.

Count the number of slates or tiles on the roof. Weigh one slate, then work out the total mass of all the slates.

Holding the slates and tiles

Slates are fixed using two nail holes which are either at the head or the centre of the slate.

head nailing

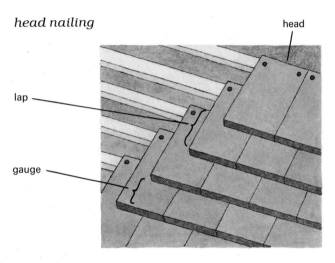

centre nailing

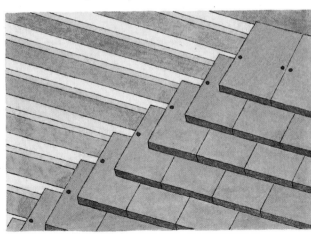

Centre nailing holds the slate better, but head-nailing protects the nails better against damp.

Tiles are hung like slates.

Look for the holes in slates and tiles.

Look for patterns in bricks

Walls

Floors and pathways

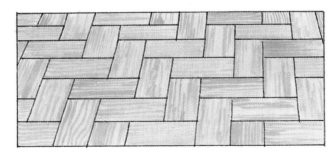

Look for patterns in tiles

Hanging

Floors

kitchen

conservatory

Make some tiling patterns

It is easy to create tiling patterns of your own if you use squared paper. The diagrams below show how to construct two types of tile.

based on a rectangle

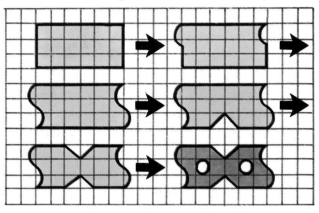

based on a parallelogram

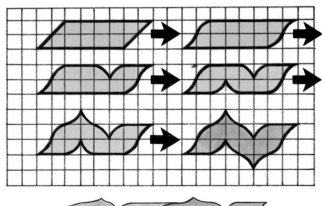

Collect rocks and pebbles from your area. Make a labelled display of them in box lids.

paper-hanky background

Bluebell wood

Jean's garden

Hole in road

In order to test the rocks you will need:

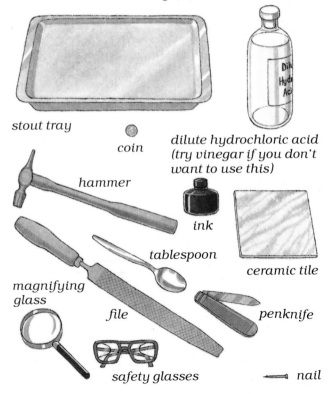

stout tray

coin

dilute hydrochloric acid (try vinegar if you don't want to use this)

hammer

ink

tablespoon

ceramic tile

magnifying glass

file

penknife

safety glasses

nail

Try to include some limestone in your sample.

Rock tests

1　Rub the rock against your cheek. Is it rough or smooth?

2　Look at the rock through your magnifying glass. Is it made up of small particles?

3　Rub the rock with your finger. Rub hard. Does any rock rub off? Look closely at your finger.

4　Break off a small piece of rock. Put it in a plastic bag. Hit it repeatedly with a hammer until it is broken up into tiny pieces.

Examine the crushed rock. Is it powdery or grainy? That is to say, does it feel fine or does it feel coarse?

5　Examine the fine particles from test 4 with a magnifying glass. What colour are they? Is there more than one colour? Is the colour the same as the outside of the rock?

6 *Use a coin, nail, penknife or some other scratcher to find out whether your rock is hard or soft. Remember, a scratch cuts into a surface not just marks it.*

A German geologist, Friedrick Mohs, devised a scale of hardness where he used ten minerals from the softest through to the hardest.

Diamond	10	Apatite	5
Corundum	9	Fluorspar	4
Topaz	8	Calcite	3
Quartz	7	Gypsum	2
Felspar	6	Talc	1

Each rock in the scale will scratch the ones below itself. The ones above will be too hard to scratch.

You can buy a mineral hardness test set from any scientific suppliers. They invariably leave out diamond!

7 *Put a drop of dilute hydrochloric acid on your rock. If it fizzes, the rock contains lime.*

Limestone rocks contain calcium carbonate. The acid reacts with this, releasing carbon dioxide.

8 *Hit each of your rocks with the handle of a heavy metal tablespoon. Hold the spoon loosely. Do you get:*
a high pitch
a low pitch
a metallic sound?

Can you sort your rocks by the sound you get?

9 *Will your rocks take up water?*

Soak them overnight in coloured water. Chip each one open in the morning. Has the water soaked in?

10 *Chip off a piece of rock. Compare the inside colour with the outside colour.*

Keep a record

	Test 1	Test 2	Test
Rock 1			
Rock 2			

How heavy?

Take four different kinds of rock from your collection. Choose ones of roughly the same size. Put them in order of heaviness by handling.

Check this by weighing.

Rock 1	Rock 2	Rock 3	Rock 4
g	g	g	g

To make a more careful comparison you need to find the volume of each rock and compare the mass of a unit volume.

Find the volume by immersing the rock in water.

Find the heaviness by weighing the rock.

For example,
   if the rock weighs X grams
   and its volume is Y cm³
then its mass per unit volume is $\frac{X}{Y}$ grams

Igneous, sedimentary and metamorphic rocks

Igneous comes from the Latin word meaning fire. Molten material from inside the earth cools to form igneous rock.

Rocks that cool quickly have a large crystalline structure. Rocks that cool slowly have small crystals.

Compare basalt and granite.

basalt (formed by quick cooling)

granite (formed by slow cooling)

Sedimentary rock is made of the small particles washed down by rivers and streams. These settle and over a long period of time are compacted to form the rock.

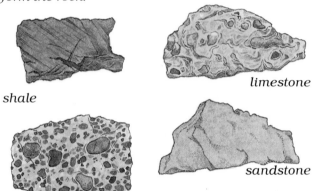

shale

limestone

conglomerate (stones and pebbles in sandstone or limestone)

sandstone

Metamorphic rocks are the result of great heat and pressure.

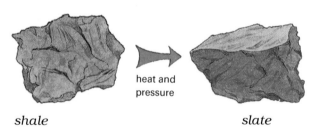

shale   heat and pressure   slate

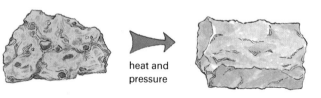

limestone   heat and pressure   marble

Soils are made from fine particles of rock mixed with organic material (see 'An Early Start to Nature', page 58).

Pebble polishers are readily available from scientific suppliers. They are simple to use.

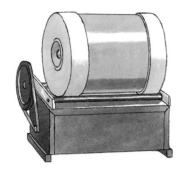

Essentially they consist of a cylindrical container in which the pebbles and an abrasive, silicon carbide grit, are placed. The container is kept tumbling by a motor.

1 Load the container about three-quarters full with a mixture of large, medium and small pebbles.

Add two heaped teaspoons of coarse grit. Cover with water. Fit the lid and squeeze its centre to expel any air.

2 Dry the outside of the container and put it on the tumbler.

Tumble for 24 hours. Stop the tumbler and press the lid to release any gases. Continue tumbling and releasing the gases for a week.

3 Wash the pebbles. Clean out the container and repeat the tumbling, but this time using fine grit.

This fine polishing will take at least another week, but it could take longer. Remember to release the gases daily.

granite   polished granite pebble

red sandstone   polished red-sandstone pebble

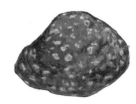   

red serpentine   polished red-serpentine pebble

banded jasper   polished banded-jasper pebble

4 Wash and rinse the pebbles and put them back in the container with one tablespoonful of polishing powder. This is usually cerium or tin oxide powder. Some people also add two tablespoons of cork chips as a buffer between the pebbles.

Cover with water. Tumble for another week.

piece of amber   polished amber pebble

   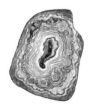

moss agate   polished moss-agate pebble

chalcedony   polished chalcedony pebble

The best effects are achieved with hard rocks – those with a hardness of over five on Mohs' scale.

There is a complex network of canals throughout the British Isles, with broad and narrow waterways, and large ship canals.

If you have a local canal the first thing is to find out where it goes.

Principal waterways of England and Wales

▬▬▬	broad
─────	narrow
═════	independent waterways

Scotland

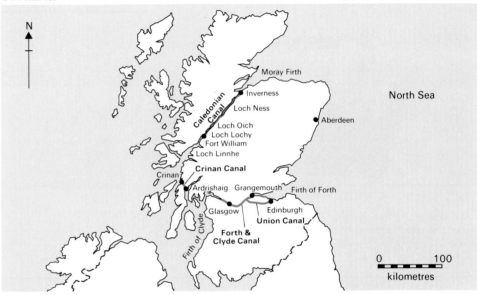

Structure and working of a lock

Make your own sketches.

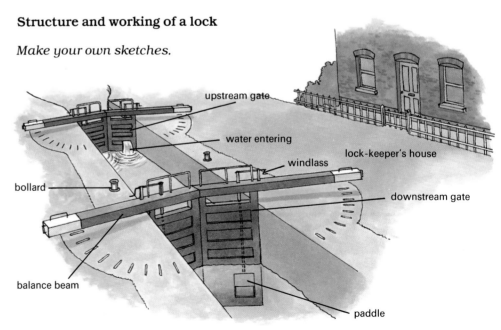

The windlass raises the paddle to let water into or out of the lock.

1 *Red boat enters the lock.*

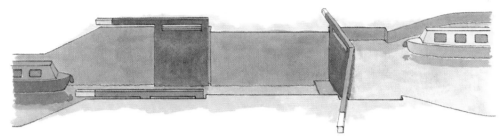

2 *Doors close. Lock keeper opens paddle on upstream door.*

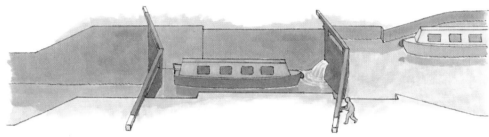

3 *Water fills lock. Lock keeper opens upstream door.*

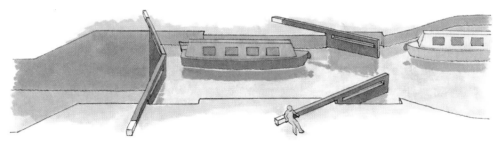

4 *Red boat leaves lock.*

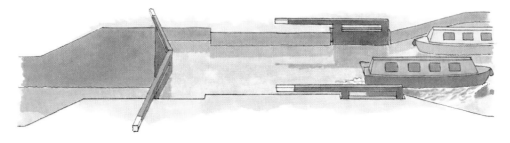

5 *Yellow boat enters lock.*

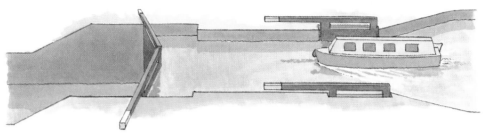

6 *Lock keeper closes upstream door and opens paddle on the downstream door.*

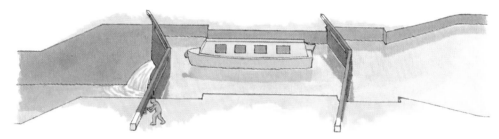

7 *Water leaves the lock. Lock keeper opens downstream door.*

8 *Yellow boat leaves lock.*

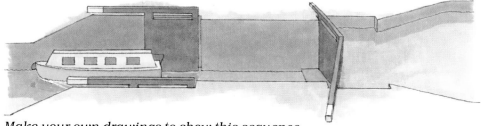

Make your own drawings to show this sequence.

Another feature of interest for children is canal boats. They make interesting subjects for sketching and modelling.

canal tug

diesel barge

short boat

narrow boat

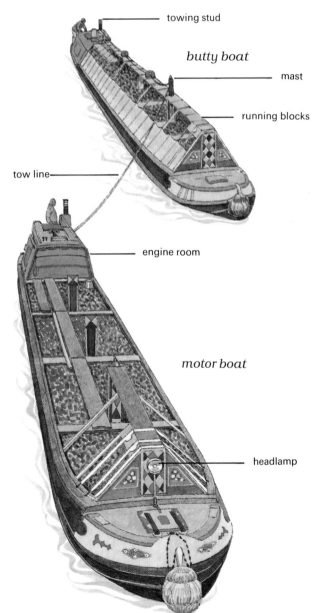

towing stud

butty boat

mast

running blocks

tow line

engine room

motor boat

headlamp

horse's tail

VALLEY

colourful nameplates

KENNET BOAT COMPANY
Horse Boats
NEWBURY

In the past, people worked and lived on their canal boats. The family was the working unit.

Working a pair of narrow boats needed someone to look after the engine, a person in charge of the butty and someone to do the locking. Perhaps Dad driving, Mum steering the butty and one of the children locking.

The people loved colour and were often very houseproud. Brightly coloured canal utensils, shining brasswork and skilfully tied rope work were the hallmark of the canal people.

All drinking water had to be carried because it was not safe to drink canal water.

water barrel

dipper

water jug

traditional rope work

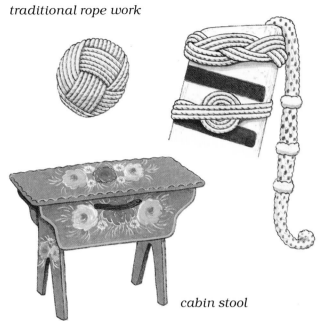

cabin stool

cabin door panel

Make your own canal paintings

Try painting in the style of the canal people.

They loved roses, perhaps because they had no gardens of their own. Castles on door panels are another feature, probably because they are large and spacious, in contrast to the cramped narrow boats.

Cover a plastic bucket with white cartridge paper. Stick it firmly to the bucket sides with flour and water paste. Trim any excess paper. Leave it to dry.

Draw on roses and other flowers. Colour them boldly.

Cut a large panel from a supermarket carton to simulate the front panel of a canal boat. Decorate it.

Make sketches of your local railway station.

Many local stations are Victorian, with cast-iron work and decorated station canopies. Modern stations use lighter materials such as aluminium and adopt a plainer style.

Look for picket fences.

Look for decorated valances.

Look for cast-iron posts.

Look for cornerstones.

Look for windows.

Look for door styles.

Look for ornamentation above windows and doors.

Look for platform seats.

Look for gables.

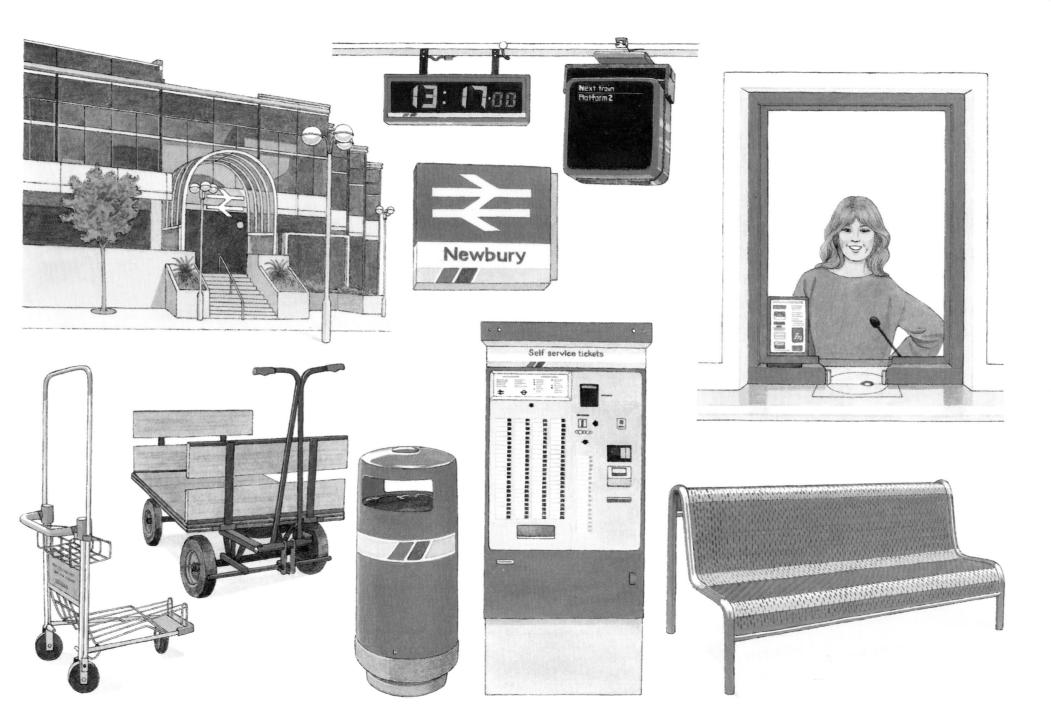

Train spotting

Trains travelling certain routes have a number at the front. Check these numbers on trains using your local station. Keep a record.

Headcode	Route
61	Dartford to Cannon Street

Tickets

Examine the details on issued tickets: class, type of ticket, date, destination and so on.

Work out the cost for a family outing to a given destination. Work out the total cost for all the families in the class to make this journey.

Logos

British Rail has a very distinctive logo.

Make a record of other logos in your area.

Design a new logo for British Rail.

Tape recordings

Tape record some of the announcements at your local station.

Record a train entering, stopping and then leaving the station.

Record a train passing straight through the station.

Posters

The railways were famous in the past for their posters advertising travel to the country and seaside.

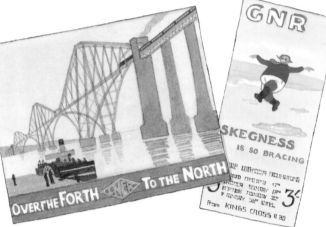

from the 1930s   *from the 1920s*

Design your own poster.

Railway history

The history and development of railways is a rich topic for research. Use the library and the local borough archives to find out about:
(a) the early railways and the engineers, navvies and contractors who worked on them
(b) the towns that grew up as a result of the railways
(c) the engines and trains
(d) the railway staff
(e) the different railway companies.

Look for features along the railway. Reminders of the past are sometimes to be found.

signal boxes

ground drops one foot
in every 490

three-aspect signal
  red – stop
  yellow – caution, proceed slowly
  green – proceed

culvert post

BRITISH TRANSPORT COMMISSION

WARNING

IS HEREBY GIVEN TO PERSONS
NOT TO TRESPASS UPON THE
RAILWAY.   PENALTY NOT
EXCEEDING **40/-**

cast-iron notices

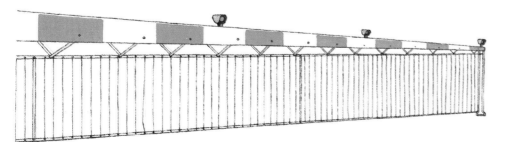

level-crossing gates

Make a passenger survey

Survey a cross-section of passengers at busy and quiet times. It may mean getting up early!

How do the results compare?

Name of station : _____ Destination : _____

Purpose of travel : _____

Frequency of travel: daily _____

                number of times per week _____

                rarely _____

Reliability of service : on time _____ late _____

Do you get a seat ? always _____ usually _____

                sometimes _____ never _____

What improvements would you like to see ? _____

Bridge survey

Most of us pause to think if asked whether there are any bridges in our area. Yet it is surprising how few places in the UK lack bridges of some kind.

Look at the 1:25 000 Ordnance Survey map for your area. Find out how the bridges are marked and see how many you can identify. There may be a railway crossing a road or water, a road crossing a road, a railway or water, and so on.

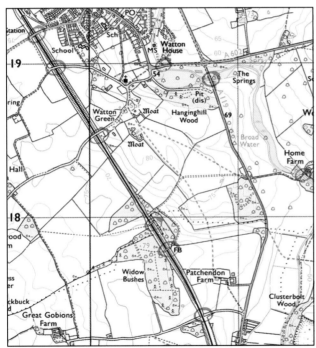

© Crown copyright

Make a record.

Name of bridge	Materials used	Rail, road or footbridge	What passes under

Sketch and/or photograph your local bridges.

Make a survey of a local bridge. Take care!

Toogood bridge	
Length	
Width	
Height	
Materials used	
Interesting facts or details	

Try making a model of the bridge (see 'An Early Start to Technology').

Bridge furnishings

Look for:

decorations

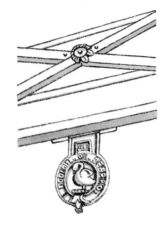

foundation stones

GELT BRIDGE
FRANCIS GILES CIVIL ENGINEER
JOHN McKAY BUILDER
MDCCCXXXII MDCCCXXXX

plaques   vehicle signs

BERKS C.C.
· BRIDGE ·
№ 243

STOP
when
lights show

masons' marks (see page 56)

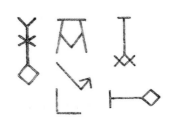

Bridge traffic

Bridges are often busy as traffic converges on them. They are ideal places for a traffic survey.

North bound 9·00 – 9·30

Traffic	Tally
Private	
Public transport	
Goods	

South bound 9·00 – 9·30

Traffic	Tally
Private	
Public transport	
Goods	

North bound 3·30 – 4·00

Traffic	Tally
Private	
Public transport	
Goods	

South bound 3·30 – 4·00

Traffic	Tally
Private	
Public transport	
Goods	

Do any patterns emerge?

Tension and compression

In any bridge some parts are in tension and some are in compression.

Suspension bridge

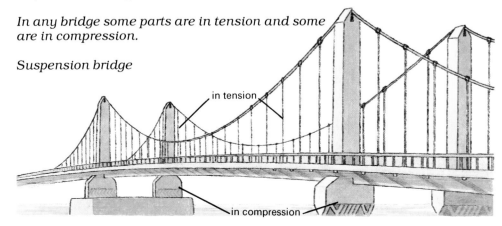

Forth railway bridge

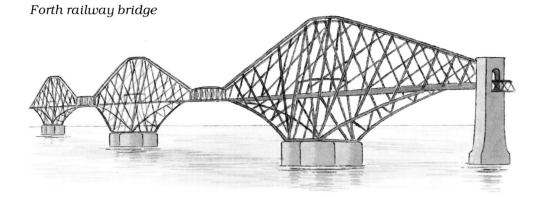

Use drinking or art straws to illustrate the forces of tension and compression.

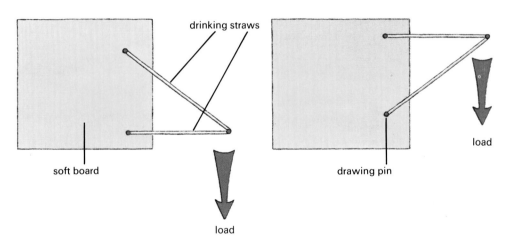

Which straws are in compression and which are in tension. Substitute a piece of cotton thread for the straw in tension in each case to check if you are correct.

Make a survey of local bridges.

Name of bridge	Part of bridge in tension	Part of bridge in compression

Choose a local factory to study. The children will be familiar with its external appearance. Parents and relatives may work there and be able to provide information. You may be able to arrange a visit.

Draw a map showing the site of the factory.

Sketch the outside of the factory.

Make up a questionnaire.

Name of factory

Address

Number of employees

Products manufactured

Raw materials used – Kind
           – obtained from

Power supplies – Kind
          – obtained from

Water supplies – special needs
          – obtained from

Waste products

Market for finished products

Transport used

Why it is located where it is

Make a survey

What do people think of the factory's effect on:
    local employment
    traffic
    pollution.

Sketch some of the transport used around the factory.

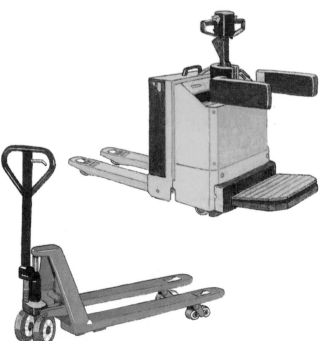

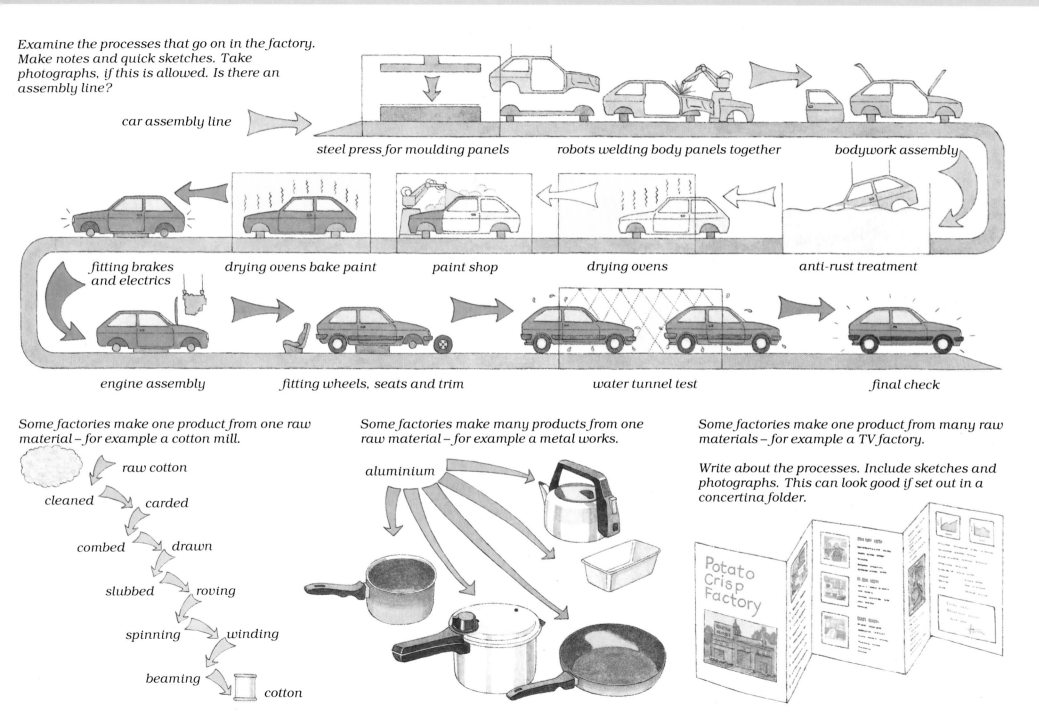

Examine the processes that go on in the factory. Make notes and quick sketches. Take photographs, if this is allowed. Is there an assembly line?

car assembly line

steel press for moulding panels

robots welding body panels together

bodywork assembly

fitting brakes and electrics

drying ovens bake paint

paint shop

drying ovens

anti-rust treatment

engine assembly

fitting wheels, seats and trim

water tunnel test

final check

Some factories make one product from one raw material – for example a cotton mill.

raw cotton

cleaned

carded

combed

drawn

slubbed

roving

spinning

winding

beaming

cotton

Some factories make many products from one raw material – for example a metal works.

aluminium

Some factories make one product from many materials – for example a TV factory.

Write about the processes. Include sketches and photographs. This can look good if set out in a concertina folder.

Potato Crisp Factory

Post boxes

Use a 1:10 000 Ordnance Survey map to plot the position of the main post office for your area. Mark in the sub-post offices. Then plot the position of the post boxes.

© Crown copyright

Make a model post box. Corrugated card will stand up well if bent into a cylinder.

Paint and decorate the post box. Make an information panel for it.

Measure the sides of the information panel on a post box and draw it full size. Position the information accurately. Try to copy the style of lettering and numbering.

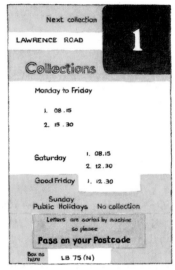

Look for the royal cipher on the box.

Make drawings or rubbings. Try and collect ciphers from the different reigns.

Postcodes

Find out the postcode of each member of the class.

Name	Address	Postcode

You can check postcodes at larger Post Offices, or in libraries, in the blue Postcode Directories. You will also find postcodes in Thomson's Local Directories.

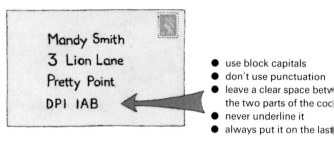

- use block capitals
- don't use punctuation
- leave a clear space betw the two parts of the cod
- never underline it
- always put it on the last

Make a letter-balance

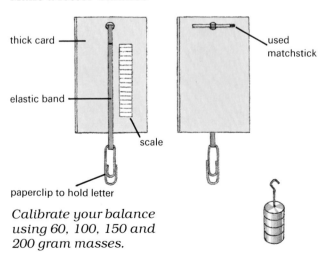

Calibrate your balance using 60, 100, 150 and 200 gram masses.

Find out first and second class postal rates for each of these masses from a Post Office or a book of stamps.

Find out how quickly mail can be delivered from your local area. Your local Post Office will have the information.

There are some cities to which first-class mail travels for next day delivery, if posted before the last collection, over and above the red areas on the adjacent map.

This map shows how quickly first-class mail can be delivered from the London Postal Districts marked with dots.

First Class Mail	
Destination	Post by
	17.00
	15.00
	12.00
	09.00
	No next day delivery

local postal district

Rivers, like canals, need putting in context. Where do they come from and where do they go?

main crossing points of the Thames

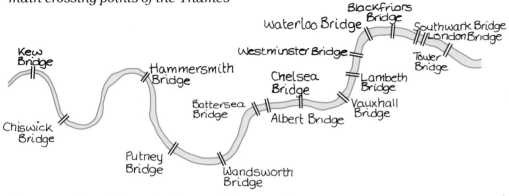

A town is often at a particular position on a river for a good reason. What about your town?

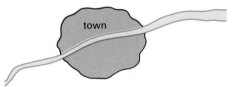

Is it a good crossing point?

Is it a port or a holiday resort at the mouth of the river?

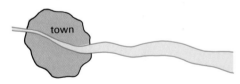

Is it because it is at the highest navigable point of the river?

Is it because it is placed at the confluence of two rivers?

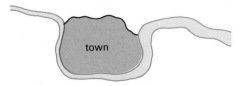

Is it because it has grown up in the bend of a river, where it is well protected?

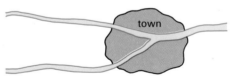

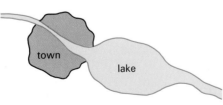

Is it a town which has grown up at the head of a lake?

Crossing points are one of the most prominent features on any river. Make sketches of local bridges.

Look for plant and animal life associated with the river (see 'An Early Start to Nature', pages 48–55).

Measure the river's speed of flow

Fix two poles 100 metres apart as markers. Throw a stout piece of twig into the centre of the water upstream of the markers. Time the twig over the 100 metre distance.

Make sketches and take photographs of local river craft.

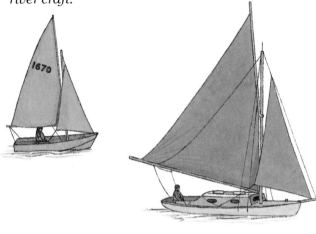

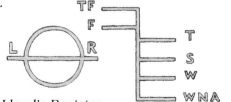

Look for the Plimsoll line markings on the sides of ships.

LR   Lloyd's Register
TF   Tropical Fresh Water
F   Fresh Water
T   Tropical
S   Summer
W   Winter
WNA Winter North Atlantic

Floating and sinking

Investigate floating and sinking. A large plastic aquarium is an ideal container to use. Make a collection of things to test.

Let the children guess whether things will float or sink. Let them suggest how things will float. Keep records.

Guess	Actual
▭	▭
⬭	⬭
◗	◗

Make some floaters to demonstrate how salt water affects the way ships float.

balsa wood strip with drawing-pin load

cigar container loaded with sand

drinking straw with Plasticine and loaded with a piece of wire

Mark a scale on the side of your floater.

Try them in tap water and in salty water.

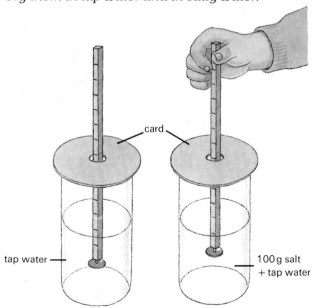

card

tap water

100 g salt + tap water

In any farm visit it is usually the farm animals that interest children the most. The farmer and family, together with the farmhouse, come a close second.

Things to do

1 (a) *Trace an outline of the farm including roads and fields from a 1:10 000 Ordnance Survey map.*
   (b) *Put the name of the farm, its map reference, at the top of your outline.*
   (c) *Give the acreage of the farm.*
   (d) *Record the number of fields.*

2 *Collect information on the names of the farmer and family. Are they tenants or owners? Include names and duties of other farm workers.*

3 *Describe the physical nature of the farm. Is it a lowland, downland, hill or mountain farm?*

4 *Is the soil light and sandy, loamy or clayey?*

5 *Describe the type of farming that goes on. Is it arable, grazing or mixed? Clay soil is often put down to grass for dairying because it is harder to work than a light arable soil.*

6 *Make quick sketches of the different types of field boundaries, such as fences, walls and hedges.*

The farm and its buildings

1 *Take photographs of the farmhouse.*

2 *Find out when it was built.*

3 *Describe the kinds of materials used to build it.*

4 *Photograph other buildings, such as the stables, barns, piggery, chicken runs and cow shed.*

5 *Photograph farm machinery.*

6 *List the farm supplies seen, such as fertilizers, lime and seed stock.*

7 *Record the types of livestock and their numbers.*

Plants

Take samples of the main crops grown back to school for examination and drawing.

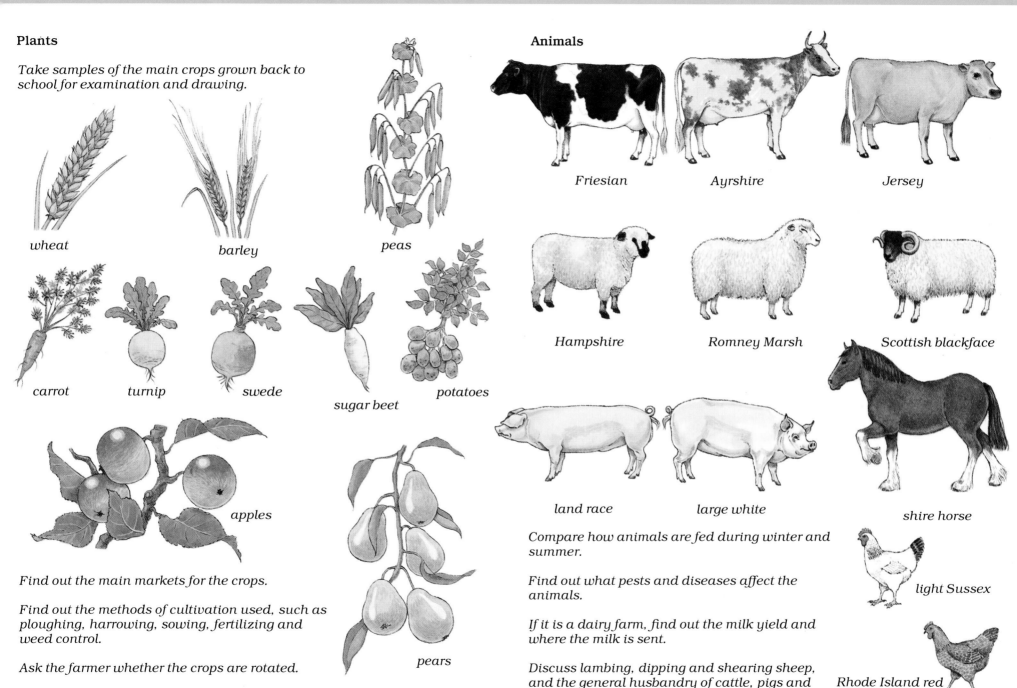

wheat

barley

peas

carrot

turnip

swede

sugar beet

potatoes

apples

pears

Find out the main markets for the crops.

Find out the methods of cultivation used, such as ploughing, harrowing, sowing, fertilizing and weed control.

Ask the farmer whether the crops are rotated.

Look at harvesting machinery.

Animals

Friesian

Ayrshire

Jersey

Hampshire

Romney Marsh

Scottish blackface

land race

large white

shire horse

light Sussex

Rhode Island red

Compare how animals are fed during winter and summer.

Find out what pests and diseases affect the animals.

If it is a dairy farm, find out the milk yield and where the milk is sent.

Discuss lambing, dipping and shearing sheep, and the general husbandry of cattle, pigs and horses.

Most people are familiar with nature trails. They are walks along a marked route, with numbered stopping points, or stations, placed at intervals.

Each person following the trail usually has a leaflet and at each station stops to read about something of interest to be seen there. Children following a trail are often asked to make drawings and answer questions.

Widening the scope of a trail to include other aspects of the environment, as well as natural ones, makes an interesting assignment.

A good starting point is to make a map of the area you propose to study. An Ordnance Survey map can be a great help, but a local town plan or street guide might be equally useful.

A walk around the area with the children may lead to suggestions of items worthy of inclusion in the trail guide. Back at school, these will probably need discussing and refining, and some may even be discarded. Keep the stations on the route to a reasonable number.

Include some natural-history clues. Remind children that these can include information about soils, rocks, pebbles, weather and so on, as well as plants and animals.

Station 2
This is a lime tree. Pick a leaf. Does it feel sticky? The sweet sticky stuff – that comes off on your fingers – is droppings from tiny flies called aphids. These like lime leaves. Draw a leaf. You will find one half does not exactly match the other – it is asymmetrical.

Station 3
Look at the concrete in the pavement. Can you see a footprint? Make a sketch of it. What sort of animal do you think made it. How many toes did it have? Can you see any claw marks?

Station 4

Have one or two clues that intrigue.

Try and include at least one clue that entails feeling something.

Station 4

Feel the texture of the facing bricks on the wall at the top of the High Street. Compare them with the stone on the shop front next to the wall. Make a rubbing of each.

Include some information about buildings, for instance,
a style of architecture
building materials
something on the building.

Station 5

This is the lightning conductor. Its lower end is earthed and if you look at the very top of the building you will see that its upper end is pointed and placed as high as possible. In our encyclopaedia it says "The action of a lightning conductor is two fold: preventive and protective. A highly charged cloud induces a strong charge on the point which flows away in the form of an electric wind and tends to neutralise the cloud in the vicinity of the building. If this action fails to stop a flash, the discharge will pass down the conductor, the easiest route to earth, instead of the building."

Make a sketch of your map. Mark in the stations. Write up the clues, information or instructions for each station as a leaflet. Design an attractive cover.

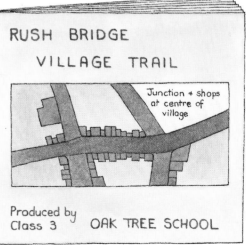

RUSH BRIDGE
VILLAGE TRAIL

Junction + shops at centre of village

Produced by Class 3   OAK TREE SCHOOL

Try your trail out on other children and classes.

The effects of pollution are visible for children to record: debris dumped along river banks, river and pond water polluted with oil or detergent. Such events are part of the modern world. Noise pollutes too, be it as blaring radios or low-flying aircraft.

Recording and discussing such events are an essential part of environmental studies. The following activities will help develop ideas about the nature of pollution, and the need for protection and conservation of our environment.

Pollution of trees and bushes

Roadside plants can suffer heavily from pollution.

<u>*Sample A*</u>

Collect fifty leaves from a roadside bush or tree. Privet hedges are often to hand.

<u>*Sample B*</u>

Find a similar bush or tree well away from road-traffic pollution and collect another fifty leaves.

Wash each leaf of sample A thoroughly in water. Use a clean paint brush. Clean <u>both</u> sides of each leaf.

Filter the resultant liquid.

Let the filter paper dry and examine the surface.

Follow the same procedure with sample B. Compare the results.

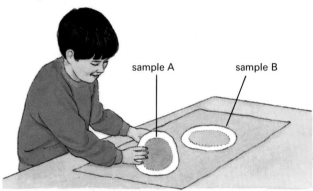

sample A   sample B

Compare bushes at different distances from the road.

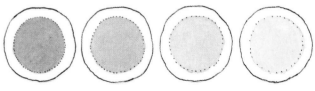

1 metre   2 metres   3 metres   4 metres

Pollution on the doorstep

Ask the children to remove their shoes and wipe the soles scrupulously clean with a damp cloth and then put their clean shoes back on.

Now take the class for a walk around the school grounds.

On returning, brush the debris from the sole of each shoe into a bowl of water. Each child, in turn, uses the same brush. At the end scrub the brush hairs on the side of the bowl to clean it.

filter paper

shoe deposit from walk

Filter the water and dry the filter paper.

Clean the shoes again with a damp cloth. Repeat the walk, only this time wipe your feet thoroughly on a doormat as you enter the building.

Brush the debris into a bowl of water as before. Filter the water.

Compare this filter paper with the first one. What conclusions do you draw?

How do wet days compare with dry days?

Sounds noisy

A loudly ticking clock can prevent us from getting off to sleep.

Devise tests to compare different ways of muffling the sound.

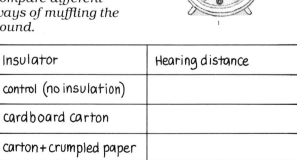

Insulator	Hearing distance
control (no insulation)	
cardboard carton	
carton + crumpled paper	
carton + tea towels	
carton + cushions	

Oil slicks

These are only too common in our seas. Try different ways of dispersing oil spillages.

Pour some oil on to salty water.

Treat the polluted water in different ways:

add sawdust   add washing up liquid

add bits of polystyrene   add talcum powder

Stir each mixture gently. Keep a record of what happens.

Bowl no.	Treatment	What happened?		
		After 5 mins	After 60 mins	After 24 hours

Make lists of the different types of local leisure facilities.

Outdoor recreation and amusements	
Facility	Names
parks / gardens	
football grounds	
dog racing	
speedway	
bowls	
tennis	

Indoor amusements	
Facility	Names
bingo	
theatres	
ten pin bowling	
skating	
gymnasia	
cinemas	

Children's recreations	
Facility	Names
parks / gardens	
adventure playgrounds	
swimming baths	
football	
clubs	
theatres	

Grown-ups recreations	
Facility	Names
public houses	
restaurants	
clubs	
betting shops	
dance halls	
concert halls	

Street games

Make a survey of street games that are still played. 'Children's Games in Street and Playground' by I. & P. Opie (published by Oxford University Press) is a good reference.

Starting a game dips etc.	Chasing games	Catching games	Seeking games
Dip, dip, dip my blue ship	touch	Please Mr Porter may we cross your water	hide and seek
One potato, two potato	French touch		sardines

Racing games	Duelling games	Strength games	Dares
last one there is a sissy	elbows	tug of war	truth or dare
peep behind the curtain	piggy back fights	tussles	follow my leader

Guessing games	Acting games	Make believe games	Hunting games
film stars	old man in the well	mothers and fathers	paper chase
I sent my son John	fox and chickens	playing schools	hare and hounds

Leisure time

Make a survey of how each child in the class spent leisure time out of the house last week. Start with Sunday and work back through the week.

Day	Place	Activity
Sunday		
Saturday		
Friday		
Thursday		
Wednesday		
Tuesday		
Monday		

Make a survey form to ask parents what they think of local recreational facilities. Here is a suggestion.

Facility	Last used	Doesn't interest me	Satisfied	Not sure	Dissatisfied	Why dissatisfied
Cinema						
Bingo						
Theatre						
Pub						
Other						

What trends are there? Which adult facilities are most popular? Which draw most criticism? Why are most people dissatisfied? Can you suggest any remedies?

The entry of electricity and gas into homes is often unobtrusive because the cables and pipes are underground. However, most children are aware that there are meters to read the amounts of the two supplies used in their homes and that they are often housed under the stairs.

power station

11 000 volt input

240 volt output

substation

Electricity supply

Look for electricity pylons carrying the power supply from the power station. Are there any in your area?

Make sketches. Think about where the forces act in such a structure. The thicker parts will be in compression and the thinner members in tension.

The electricity leaving the power station has to be at sufficient pressure to carry it through the network. It therefore leaves the power station at 400 000 or 275 000 volts. Substations reduce the voltage to the 240 volts used in the home.

Are there any substations near you?

400 000 or 275 000 volts

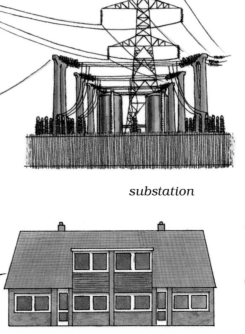

132 000 volts

11 000 volt output

substation

substation

home

Meters

Ask the children to draw the electricity and gas meters in their homes. Are they the new digital meters or the old dial-type ones?

electricity meter

gas meter

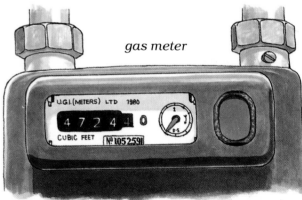

Make a graph showing the main forms of heating used in the children's homes.

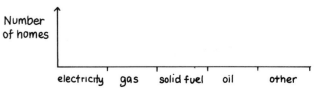

Number of homes

electricity   gas   solid fuel   oil   other

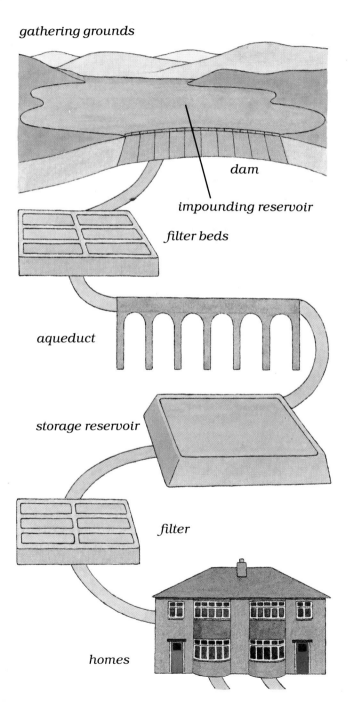

gathering grounds

dam

impounding reservoir

filter beds

aqueduct

storage reservoir

filter

homes

The water supply, like the electricity and gas supplies, is mostly hidden away from view.

In the past, people depended on well, spring and river water. With the increase in population and a more sophisticated way of life (a flush toilet uses 9 litres of water per flush), there has been a need to build reservoirs and a more complex supply system.

A large town may well have impounding reservoirs some distance from the town, usually in hilly country. Water leaving these reservoirs is filtered before it is transported along an aqueduct to storage reservoirs near the town. The water is filtered again before it leaves these reservoirs for homes.

Look for signs of the water supply in your area. Storage reservoirs and water towers are the most obvious ones. There may be a water works with its filter beds near you.

Water towers

These are very distinctive and supply a good head of water to flat areas.

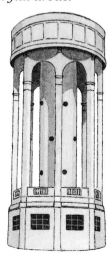

Sketch any in your region.

Filters

Make a filter using a 3 litre plastic lemonade bottle, sand and chippings.

cut off the base

fine sand

coarse sand

small chippings

muddy water

muslin tied over neck

yoghurt pot

Test the filter by passing muddy water through it.

Stop taps

Every home has a water stop tap. It is on the main pipe bringing water into the house. Ask the children to locate the one in their home.

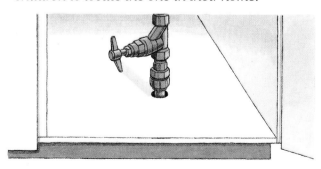

E. J. Arnold and Son Ltd
Dewsbury Road
Leeds, LS11 5TD

Telephone: 0532 772112

Griffin and George Ltd
Bishops Meadow Road
Loughborough
Leicestershire, LE11 0RG

Telephone: 0509 233344

Philip Harris Ltd
Lynn Lane
Shenstone
Staffordshire, WS14 0EE

Telephone: 0543 480077

Berol Ltd
Oldmedow Road
Kings Lynn
Norfolk, PE30 4JR

Telephone: 0553 761221